A Sick Business

The Stockholm Network

The Stockholm Network is a one-stop shop for organisations seeking to work with Europe's brightest policy-makers and thinkers. Our unique network of over 100 market-oriented think tanks in Europe and farther afield provides unparalleled access to the best European policy thinking, the opportunity to lead debates, to change the climate of ideas in Europe, and to meet the key players in shaping the policy debates of tomorrow.

The Stockholm Network is funded by subscriptions from companies, think tanks and individuals. Its subscribers span a range of industries including pharmaceutical companies. This publication was commissioned by the Stockholm Network and is funded from its general income.

A Sick Business

Counterfeit medicines and organised crime

Graham Satchwell

Foreword by Lord Mackenzie of Framwellgate

First published in Great Britain in 2004 by
The Stockholm Network
35 Britannia Row
London N1 8QH
www.stockholm-network.org

in association with Profile Books Ltd

The Stockholm Network is Europe's only dedicated service
organisation for market-oriented think tanks and thinkers

A CIP catalogue record for this book is available from the
British Library.

ISBN 0 9547663 2 6

Designed by Sue Lamble
Typeset in Stone Serif by MacGuru Ltd
info@macguru.org.uk

Printed and bound in Great Britain by Hobbs the Printers

Contents

About the author

Graham Satchwell is a former detective superintendent and has held senior security executive positions within several global corporations. The former Association of Chief Police Officers' spokesperson on the counterfeiting of branded goods, he was the main author and driving force behind the Memorandum of Understanding signed in 1999 between the police service, HM Customs, trading standards authorities and brand-owners. Before leaving the police service, Graham received the thanks of four government ministers for his work, and in his time has been commended by judges, chief constables, the Director of Public Prosecutions and the Lord Lieutenant of London for successful major investigations.

Since leaving the police in 1999, he has successfully managed international and politically sensitive major corporate invest-igations into counterfeiting, illegal diversion and fraud, including the massive reimportation of anti-retroviral drugs from Africa to Europe. Two years ago he created and led an anti-counterfeiting investigative forum involving the world's leading pharmaceutical companies in Europe.

Graham now leads Proco Solutions (www.Procosolutions.

com), a specialist consultancy that provides brand protection to brand-owners. He is a law graduate and a fellow of the Royal Society of Arts.

Foreword
Lord Mackenzie of Framwellgate

When I was approached at the beginning of 2004 by the Stockholm Network to propose someone to look into the issue of counterfeit medicines, I had no hesitation in recommending Graham Satchwell. I have been acquainted with Graham for a number of years and know him to be one of only a few individuals truly knowledgeable in this area. He is a very experienced investigator.

Some will be aware of Sir David Hare's play *The Permanent Way*, which had a very good run this year at the National Theatre. This play centres on the exceptionally thorough, major police investigation that took place into the Southall train crash. It revolves around the conflict between the political, personal, commercial and public interests that coloured that investigation. The words spoken in the play are reported as being a verbatim record of what the real participants said. Those who have seen the play would have been struck by the integrity, intelligence and commitment of the senior investigating officer. Few would know that this was Graham Satchwell. Those who do know him would not be surprised that I thought him appropriate to the task of researching and writing on this important topic.

Now that the paper is finished, I feel vindicated. For the first time, evidence is drawn from experts in diverse fields to support an alarming proposition – that thousands of people in the UK, and elsewhere in Europe, could be putting their lives at risk daily through using fake medicines. It is a massive proposition, yet the need for change and greater prevention is clearly demonstrated.

September 2004

Preface

I have spent about ten years in the business of preventing and tackling the problem of counterfeited branded goods. Sometimes the trade appears innocuous, though in truth it rarely is.

The business of counterfeiting medicines is, in any sensible evaluation of the problem of counterfeiting, a special case. The subject involves the interests of several government departments – Health, Trade and Industry, the Home Office and the Foreign Office. Those various interests are multiplied in the commercial world and then interface with the various government departments in many ways. The position in the UK is largely reflected in other countries and then complicated further by the involvement of the EU in its pan-European regulatory role. Perhaps that is why reaching an informed position from a wide perspective is so difficult.

All the facts necessary for a reasonable understanding of the nature and scope of the dangers of pharmaceutical counterfeiting, and its potential effects on the health of the population, have been readily available. What has been necessary is for someone to 'join up the dots' and obtain the necessary media coverage.

In order to make significant change, and to take reasonable steps to protect the public, coordinated action will be necessary. But before that can happen, interested parties, particularly pharmaceutical companies, parallel traders, the police and the Crown Prosecution Service, will need to understand the urgency.

I came to write this paper through the recommendation of Lord Mackenzie of Framwellgate. I thank him for the opportunity to address this important topic. Helen Disney of the Stockholm Network identified the need for the subject to be properly explored, and Ed Randall, about to start a career in law, acted as my researcher. I thank them both.

Graham Satchwell

September 2004

Glossary of terms

Counterfeit medicines

Medicines which have been deliberately and fraudulently mislabelled with respect to their identity and/or source. Counterfeiting can apply to both branded and generic products and may include products with the correct ingredients but fake packaging, with the wrong ingredients, without active ingredients or with insufficient active ingredients.

Diversion

Diversion is the movement of branded goods across international markets, contrary to the wishes and legal rights of the brand-owner. The word 'diversion' cannot be used for the unwanted (by the brand-owner) movement of goods within the European Union, as it is legally a single market. Sometimes the word 'grey' is used to describe diverted products.

Grey products

See 'Diversion'

Intellectual property rights (IPRs)

Limited rights conferred by governments over original intellectual creations (e.g. patents which protect inventions, copyrights which protect expressions of ideas and trademarks which protect brands). IPRs are bound by the geographical boundaries of each state: the principle of 'national exhaustion' means that the IPR holders' rights are extinct upon first sale within national borders (i.e. anyone who buys a product can do what he likes with it afterwards, within that country). By contrast, international exhaustion terminates rights upon first sale anywhere. This would mean that someone who buys a product in one country could export it and have it re-imported elsewhere without contravening the original owner's IPR.

Organised crime

The term 'organised crime' is variously defined. The UK National Criminal Intelligence Service would recognise the following terms. Organised crime refers to the activities of any group which comes together to commit serious crime (serious crime in this context means crime for which the offenders could expect to receive at least three years' imprisonment). In some instances such groups consist of permanent members (each with a distinct role, and within a hierarchy in which there are clear lines of command and communication), but the term also includes loose networks, whose members undertake particular criminal ventures of varying complexity, structure and duration. In the latter instance some of the criminals may not think of themselves as being members of an organised crime group.

Parallel trade (re-importation)

Parallel trade (known as re-importation in the USA) occurs when products protected by patent, trademark or copyright are first placed into circulation in one market, then (re-)imported into a second market by a person other than the original owner of the intellectual property rights and against the original owner's interests. A variety of products are traded in this way, including pharmaceuticals, automobiles, clothing, perfume and other consumer goods. Parallel trade is legal within the European Union.

Substandard medicines

Products whose composition and ingredients do not meet the correct scientific specifications and which are consequently ineffective and often dangerous to the patient. Substandard products may occur as a result of negligence, human error, insufficient human and financial resources or counterfeiting. Counterfeit medicines are part of the broader phenomenon of substandard pharmaceuticals.

1

Introduction

Evidence shows an increase in production, distribution and sale worldwide of counterfeit, spurious and substandard medicines which do not comply with any quality standards. Such products are a waste of money for the people who buy them, prolong treatment periods, exacerbate the conditions being treated, increase the emergence of drug resistance and can even cause death.[1]

This paper reviews a hypothesis that needs to be tested in the interests of public safety. It is as follows:

➤ Counterfeiting of pharmaceuticals is a global trade.

➤ This trade is conducted by unscrupulous people whose actions have already cost thousands of lives.

➤ We live in a world of increasing global trade which now provides direct access to counterfeit pharmaceuticals via the Internet both for personal use and commercial supply.

➤ Europe and North America provide the best return on investment for those involved in the international supply of counterfeit products.

➤ The free movement of pharmaceuticals within Europe, and the current need for repackaging (in the appropriate language), makes it easier for counterfeit pharmaceuticals to be sold through the legitimate distribution chain and supplied to our hospitals and pharmacies.

➤ There is no effective method within the UK – or to a greater or lesser extent across Europe – of identifying counterfeited pharmaceuticals before they are dispensed.

➤ It is at least likely that some counterfeit products have been administered by the NHS and other health service providers, and that injury or death has been caused.

➤ The current UK 'adverse drug reaction system' is not designed for or sufficient to identify cases of counterfeit pharmaceuticals.

➤ The current UK enforcement regime is inadequate, for while regulatory agencies are not equipped to tackle international crime, within national police and intelligence agencies there is a lack of appreciation of the nature of the problem and a reluctance to use the legislation and resources available to deal with it.

➤ International counterfeiting of pharmaceuticals usually involves organised crime and sometimes involves terrorist groups and terrorist funding.

In this paper, counterfeit products are discussed alongside out-of-date stock and inadequately packaged goods. They are not always discussed separately, not always presented as entirely different entities, for in practice it is impossible to clearly separate discussions on these various ways in which dangerous pharmaceuticals can reach the patient. The unscrupulous businessman has no need to distinguish between them.

It might well be for this reason that the World Health Organisation's (WHO) factsheet on *Counterfeit and Substandard Medicines* simply uses the term 'substandard' to encompass counterfeited products. It says:

> Substandard medicines are products whose composition and ingredients do not meet the correct scientific specifications and which are consequently ineffective and often dangerous to the patient. Substandard products may occur as a result of negligence, human error, insufficient human and financial resources or counterfeiting. Counterfeit medicines are part of the broader phenomenon of substandard pharmaceuticals.[2]

The WHO factsheet goes on to define counterfeit in these terms: 'counterfeits are deliberately and fraudulently mislabelled with respect to identity and/or source. Counterfeiting can apply to both branded and generic products and counterfeit medicines may include products with the correct ingredients but fake packaging, with the wrong ingredients, without active ingredients or with insufficient active ingredients'.[3]

It is the WHO definition which is generally adopted by pharmaceutical companies. Regulators and law enforcement officers have to look to particular definitions as provided by criminal law and particular regulations.

The WHO definition of counterfeits and its broader category of 'substandard medicines' are both applicable to the arguments put forward in this work. Much is said in the pages that follow about parallel trade. It might be that most parallel traders are completely law-abiding, but as in any other occupation there will be those that are not. Certainly, the special nature of their chosen business – dealing wholesale in life-saving and potentially death-causing products – means that extra care needs to be taken, by regulators and by parallel traders themselves.

Sometimes it will be necessary to use the word 'counterfeiting' in the narrow sense. Sometimes the word 'diversion' appears. Diversion is the movement of branded goods across international markets, contrary to the wishes and legal rights of the brand-owner. The word 'diversion' cannot be used for the unwanted (by the brand-owner) movement of goods within the European Union since it is legally, in this respect at least, a single market. Sometimes the word 'grey' is used to describe diverted products.

The paper begins by describing briefly the nature of the international supply and distribution of pharmaceuticals and the nature of parallel trade. It goes on to describe the current inadequate European monitoring of parallel-traded pharmaceuticals, given the opportunity that parallel trade provides for the importation and sale of counterfeit and substandard medicines. The theoretical opportunities for such illicit trade are demonstrated by actual cases, and further corroborated by the conclusions of those organisations which ought to know of them.

It brings together medical findings, regulatory information

and details of international crimes (as well as investigations and intelligence) to highlight a current, significant risk to the health of UK and other European citizens.

Before publishing this work I copied extracts to the Medicines and Healthcare Regulatory Agency (MHRA). This seemed appropriate, as I have known members of that agency for several years and had met with old acquaintances and new during the research for this work. Just prior to publication, I received feedback from them on the draft. The MHRA have asked me to include the following statement on their behalf: 'We make the following disclaimer. That the MHRA in no way endorses this publication or supports the opinions represented.'

2

Counterfeit drugs and the Internet

The richer nations of the world, primarily America and western European countries, continue to spend more and more on medicines and health products. We live in a world of ever-increasing global trade, and every sort of health product is available to any of us with access to the World Wide Web, whether as trader or consumer.

The extent of Internet market penetration continues to deepen and widen. Within Europe, whose borders are often porous, goods can enter at any point and then enjoy the legal right to move freely between European nations.

The easy and direct availability of many foreign goods can be of tremendous benefit both to those who need the euro, pound or dollar and to Europeans themselves (particularly the British and the Germans), who can buy goods more cheaply than they are available at home.

The importation of pharmaceuticals into the UK and wider Europe by traders and individual consumers is, however, insufficiently regulated and monitored. This poses a significant health threat to our citizens, particularly the vulnerable. The public, legislators, regulators, law enforcement agencies and those involved in the manufacture, distribution and sale of pharmaceuticals need to be made more aware and to act in concert to prevent serious harm.

The current danger manifests itself in two main ways:

1 Consumers buy direct from websites that purport to be representing a UK, European or North American business. Such websites will usually suggest that a prescription is necessary and attempt to reassure the purchaser that all is legitimate. Sometimes they are legitimate – but often they are not.

2 Dangerous pharmaceuticals, obtained from abroad, become available in commercial quantities for sale through the legitimate distribution chain. They can end up being prescribed by doctors and provided by the National Health Service (or public health providers elsewhere in Europe) and supplied to the patient direct in hospital or obtained over the counter in pharmacies and dispensaries. These products are supplied innocently 'at the point of sale' by legitimate means, by those unaware of their true origin, which is sometimes, logically and demonstrably, organised crime.

These two means of supplying dangerous pharmaceuticals are, in practice, connected. Those who buy pharmaceuticals from within the EU to sell on elsewhere will be well aware that they can also order commercial quantities direct from China, Korea, India or elsewhere. In fact, there are many commercial websites catering precisely to their needs. Consequently, the Internet is not only a threat to the unwary online customer but a ready marketplace from which the unscrupulous European involved in parallel trade can buy and supply others goods obtained from within the EU and outside it.

The pharmaceuticals market is not a simple one – it is highly regulated and, being dependent on research and development, highly secretive. It is also highly profitable and ever-growing. All societies everywhere value health, and no normal person would fail to invest in the prevention of disease or the provision of cure. The pharmaceuticals market will grow as long as this remains true, and as long as wealth and life expectancy continue to increase so will investment in retaining health and vitality. Clearly, the healthcare market is one that any sensible investor, criminal or otherwise, should consider.

The modern manufacturing process within a global industry embraces 'outsourcing' opportunities. This simply means getting as much of the labour as possible done by third-party contractors. It provides flexibility and cost savings. In the pharmaceuticals market it is reflected in the provision by third-party manufacturers of both products and packaging. These are often sourced in India and elsewhere in the East.

Pharmaceutical companies obtain the bulk of their outsourced products and services in whichever country they choose, and they choose countries that are politically stable and have cheap and skilled labour and a favourable tax regime. Sadly, some such countries also have a poor record in terms of regulatory control and intellectual property rights (IPR) – China and India, for example.

The sourcing of pharmaceuticals in this way necessarily

involves the sharing of valuable information about the exact design and construction of the drugs. Similar information is also provided to those who, in such far-off places, provide the printed inserts (patient information leaflets) and outer wrappings. These arrangements provide for relatively easy access to trade secrets in cultural environments that often have little in common with our own. Governments of such countries often have no concept of consumer protection for their own citizens, let alone ours.

In such countries, the owner of the rights to manufacture (for example, Pfizer, GlaxoSmithKline, Eli Lilly, Bristol Myers Squibb) will retain the sales function in-house and representatives will endeavour to sell at the best price to national health institutions and main distributors. They will also sell to others such as private healthcare providers and international health charities. Thereafter, the manufactured product should be exported only to whichever country is designated by the IPR holder.

Those who purchase manufactured products can behave illegally in at least two ways. First, they might purchase goods intending to export them to more expensive markets, contrary to the express wishes of the IPR holder, and thus undermining the IPR holder's own sales efforts in those other countries (diversion). Second, they might purport to be charities supplying goods at cost to the needy, when in fact they intend to sell at maximum profit (fraud).

Some IPR holders, it must be said, facilitate these 'frauds' by tying the income of their sales staff too closely to quantities sold and failing to monitor excessive sales. Such cases involve countries with relatively low prices where sales staff, focusing on achieving their own salary bonuses, are prepared to sell much more product than the market can truly sustain, and others simply turn a 'blind eye'.

The country of destination will have its own particular regulatory requirements in relation to every ingredient of the product and in relation to the information that must be supplied to the consumer with the product and the language(s) in which it must be supplied. This often results in the original packaging and patient information leaflets being removed by the trader or 'diverter' and substituted with cheaper, less safe and less secure replacements. I know of no distributor, importer or trader who removes the packaging provided by the IPR holder and substitutes something that has equal or better anti-counterfeiting features.

In the UK (and elsewhere in Europe) governments have individually negotiated fixed prices in relation to hundreds of different sorts of medication. Given that some parts of Europe are poorer than others, it should be no surprise that some European governments acquire these medicines much more cheaply than, say, the Germans, British and French. Rest assured, the drug companies still make a profit – even in the cheapest markets.

In the UK, hospitals and Primary Care Trusts are encouraged by the government, as the monopoly tax-funded payer for services, to buy drugs from the cheapest possible source. They make every effort to do so – and their only method of sourcing such drugs (unless they purchase from an online company) is to buy from parallel traders. They regularly do just that.

Such 'parallel trading' – that is, purchasing branded goods in one EU member state in order to sell them in another where the normal price will be higher – is not illegal. To all intents and purposes the EU is to be regarded as having one internal market with no boundaries. This is specified in Articles 30 and 36 of the Treaty of Rome, which prohibit the use of statutory restrictions and market barriers in relation to the free movement of goods in the EU. The courts have consistently maintained this principle. Thus any licensed trader is entitled to buy goods in Greece and export them from there to Scotland. A difficulty arises, however, when language requirements in the 'recipient country' are different to those in the country from which they are being parallel-exported. There is little point in a product being received in Scotland when the packaging is clearly printed in Greek.

It is this issue which has given rise to acceptance of the need for parallel traders to repackage the product in order to comply with the regulatory requirements in countries in which the goods are marketed or distributed. In the process of repackaging, which might take place abroad, the more expensive anti-counterfeiting packaging of the manufacturer is often entirely removed, batch numbers are reprinted and patient advice material translated.

This creates five further problems:

➤ Pristine packaging is available to be used for counterfeit products, although the redundant packaging is supposed to be destroyed.

➤ Counterfeit products can easily be introduced into the distribution system, parcelled as parallel-traded.

➤ The potential for errors in translation and errors in transcription of batch numbers is introduced.

➤ In moving around Europe, sometimes passing through as many as 30 distributors, the product becomes 'anonymous' and, should it later be found to be time-expired or counterfeit, the seller can legitimately claim he was unaware of the fact.

➤ There is an increased risk of products reaching their 'use-by date' before reaching the consumer.

It has already been suggested that goods circulating within Europe sometimes come illegally from other parts of the world. These might be diverted goods, obtained by fraud, or they may be counterfeit (or stolen). On several occasions, fraudulent 'charitable' organisations have been set up to purport to be in the business of acquiring cheap pharmaceuticals for supply to parts of the world that, through poverty, cannot afford Western prices. More than once it has been shown that such organisations have obtained massive amounts of pharmaceutical product on that basis simply in order to sell them in Europe at a fat profit. This is significant for at least two reasons. First, this practice results in further deprivation to the world's poorest people – they are simply not always getting even the amount of pharmaceutical product that we think they are. Second, it gives some indication of the unscrupulous, pathological psychology of some of those behind pharmaceutical fraud. Causing danger and death to the needy is worth the profit to them, it seems. Those in western Europe and North America should not imagine that such criminals care more about Western lives than African ones. Profit alone is the usual motive.

A perfect example of introducing a mixture of diverted and

counterfeit product into the legitimate distribution chain was provided recently. Sixty million tablets of Lipitor, one of Pfizer's best-selling drugs, were recalled from pharmacies across the USA after counterfeit versions had been sold into the legitimate distribution chain mixed with 'diverted' products.[1]

3

The growth in parallel trade

Obtaining a product or substance from one country where it is relatively cheap and selling it into a country where it is relatively expensive is the basis of all international trade and has been going on for thousands of years. It has, it seems, been of benefit to both exporter and importer. To trace the history of 'diverted' and 'parallel' products is therefore a tangled matter. Certainly, the movement of branded pharmaceuticals between countries, contrary to the wishes of the rights holders (and no doubt in some cases contrary to the interests of consumers), is generations old, and not dependent on the existence of the European Union. It is generally accepted, however, that this issue arose as a matter of concern in the 1970s in Europe. As you would expect, it was those countries that provided the biggest markets – and highest prices – which were targeted by the parallel traders: the UK and Germany. Those countries are still the main importers of parallel-traded pharmaceuticals. In those days, Spain, Italy, Portugal and Greece – where pharmaceuticals could be obtained most cheaply – provided the supply. Today, while these countries are still involved, an expanded Europe provides wider opportunities for the parallel trader.

At a recent seminar on 'Parallel Trade in Medicines' organised by the Social Market Foundation think tank,[1] it was accepted that:

➤ Some 140,000,000 medicines are parallel-traded every year in the European Union.

➤ 70 per cent of these medicines are destined for the UK (over 100,000,000 medicines).

➤ The market share of parallel-traded products has increased from 11 per cent in 1999 to 17 per cent in 2003, an increase of over 50 per cent.

➤ Parallel-traded medicines now account for approximately 20 per cent of the prescriptions dispensed to patients.

➤ It is estimated that 90 per cent of UK pharmacists source some products through parallel trade.[2]

Re-import licences awarded to parallel traders (1997–2001)

	1997	1998	1999	2000	2001
Belgium	4	5	11	7	18
Netherlands	3,156	3,237	3,355	3,173	3,104
Norway	99	48	189	144	84
Sweden	45	227	341	320	135
UK	541	757	1,378	1,363	639

The growth in the numbers of parallel trade licences issued in the UK has been significant. According to the figures supplied by the Medicines and Healthcare Products Regulatory Agency (MHRA) – formerly the Medicines Control Agency (MCA) – the popularity of parallel trading in pharmaceuticals has never been higher:

1993	239
1994	266
1995	426
1996	447
1997	541
1998	757
1999	1,354
2000	1,363
2001	1,546
2002	2,014
2003	2,916[3]

Unfortunately, the MHRA has no statistics on the total amount of pharmaceutical product being imported into the UK. This information is apparently not collated anywhere, and such information as is available appears to be collated from prescriptions and other records of drugs administered and sold. What is clear, however, is that a very wide variety of pharmaceutical products is parallel-imported into the UK. Transparency over total quantities would undoubtedly be of value in assessing the extent of this trade. It is estimated that 'by the end of 2001 the parallel trade in pharmaceutical products had reached $3.3 billion in Europe and is calculated to reach $7.4 billion by 2006'.[4]

A rise in parallel trade does not necessarily mean a corresponding rise in the incidence of substandard pharmaceuticals. What is clear, however, is that the greater the number of parallel imports the greater the chance that substandard pharmaceuticals, counterfeit or otherwise, will be imported.

4

The current regulatory and enforcement regime

There are numerous organisations dedicated to ensuring quality and safety in our medicines. European countries are protected by domestic agencies (in the UK, the MHRA) and a pan-European agency (the European Medicines Agency, EMEA). Pharmaceutical manufacturers spend huge sums on testing before a new drug can be marketed. Once drugs are launched they are subject to all sorts of monitoring by clinical and 'watchdog' groups. Each new drug is flagged up within the Adverse Drug Reaction System and each new pack boldly marked with a black triangle. The MHRA and others monitor adverse reactions to new drugs carefully. The sale to the public and administering of prescribed drugs are equally well studied. The Medicines Act and secondary legislation provide for the regulation.

One might reasonably expect therefore that when a business is buying potentially life-saving and death-causing pharmaceuticals from abroad and supplying them for mass consumption in UK or elsewhere in Europe, there would be a strict regime to ensure that:

➤ Only fit persons would be allowed to conduct that business. Yet criminal records checks are not carried out on would-be licence holders or those who are legally charged with ensuring that the pharmaceuticals are safe.

➤ Once a person is convicted of selling out-of-date or counterfeit medicines they would no longer be able to carry on such business. Yet there is no such bar and no such power.

➤ A licence would be needed to permit the importation of each drug by type, brand name and quantity, yet this is not the case.

➤ Premises used for the storage and distribution of such pharmaceuticals would be frequently inspected (given that many drugs have to be stored within certain environmental strictures). In reality, premises might be visited less than once every three years. Even then, the inspections are not comprehensive but thematic and, in the vast majority of cases, the business to be inspected is given at least four weeks' notice.

One might also assume that a national system would operate to identify counterfeit or other dangerous imported pharmaceuticals. The reality is somewhat different. There is no point within our current system of controls where the quantity of pharmaceuticals entering the UK can be established or monitored. There is simply no point at which all the necessary information is collated.

The principle behind this current practice is mirrored in the MHRA *Guide to the Implementation of EC Directive 92/25*.[1] It states: 'Wholesale trading between a dealer in the UK and a buyer in Germany … should be no different … than wholesale trading between a dealer in Hertfordshire and a buyer in Essex.' The obvious difference, of course, is that the MHRA can visit and inspect premises in Essex and Hertfordshire but in relation to the manufacture and storage of products from elsewhere in Europe, which might end up in Hertfordshire or Essex, they are blind.

A wholesale licence, issued in the UK by the MHRA, enables the holder to procure, hold, supply or export any medicinal product. Each wholesale distribution licence holder must appoint a 'Responsible Person' (RP) whose role it is to ensure that the terms of the licence are complied with (though the 'Responsible Person' need *not* be a pharmacist or otherwise scientifically or professionally qualified).[2] Given that part of the role is to ensure that the terms of each product licence are complied with, this seems less than rigorous. In addition, the RP can be, but need not be, an employee of the wholesaler; equally the RP can be a consultant visiting the wholesaler's premises only when requested.

Guidance specifically informs the wholesaler that the RP is not liable in criminal law if the terms of the wholesale licence are breached. The guidance states that 'if the Responsible Person in our opinion is not adequately carrying out his duties we may have to consider suspending the licence and/or withdrawing our acceptance of him on that licence'.[3] In effect, there is no criminal penalty for failing to act responsibly as the Responsible Person.

The UK is obliged under EU rules to record the number of

licences issued, along with details of suspensions and revocations of licence. There is no indication that this power has been used within the UK. All EU states have an obligation to tell others about revocations and suspensions of licences.

When product is imported and reaches wholesalers it is often mixed with older stock or with stock that has arrived from different locations. Any total stock of individual medicinal product will therefore commonly comprise several different batch numbers (as given by the original manufacturer). Batch numbering is an important safety feature and one that manufacturers rely on in the event of there being a safety issue arising in relation to a particular batch. In that event, batch numbering facilitates a batch recall. Yet this MHRA guidance to importers and wholesalers states that 'there is no requirement in the Directive to record [manufacturers'] batch numbers'.[4] It should be noted that further specific licences are necessary for repackaging and marketing the drugs. What the wholesaler's licence enables is the import from Europe and the selling on to other dealers in the UK.

In general, the courts in Europe and the UK have been keen to support the free movement of goods across national boundaries. This approach is naturally reflected in the advice and actions of the MHRA. Several recent decisions reflect the belief in the right of traders to deal in prescription-only medicines with a minimum of interference. Take, for instance, the Court of Appeal decision in March 2004 involving a civil action taken by GlaxoSmithKline (GSK) against Dowelhurst, a major parallel trading company based in the UK. GSK argued that Aids medicines with their registered trademarks were sold at low prices on the understanding that they were for use in Africa.

Instead of being used for this humanitarian purpose the goods were being fraudulently diverted to a Swiss company which sold them on so that they came into the hands of Dowelhurst, a well-known parallel trader. Dowelhurst bought them (sixteen consignments) and sold them into the UK, where some were supplied to hospitals. Hence Dowelhurst, it was claimed, had infringed the registered trademarks. Dowelhurst argued that these were the genuine goods and were supplied in packaging that was appropriate for the European market. They even bore a European product licence number. There was nothing to suggest to anyone that they were meant for Africa or not to be sold on the European market.

This case rested, of course, on what it could be proved Dowelhurst knew. The broader facts did not come to light. What was not said was that the Aids drugs had been provided in huge quantities at low prices specifically for the poor of Francophone Africa, that the goods had been sent to Africa, where they had been stored (at least some of them, and probably all) in sweltering conditions in open-topped barns on rubbish-strewn industrial sites populated by vermin. These drugs had never reached the needy Africans but had been sold back into Europe so that greedy officials and businessmen could take advantage of the price differentials. Nor was it mentioned that a criminal prosecution of others involved was under way in Africa and elsewhere. (There was no proof that Dowelhurst were anything other than innocent recipients of these medicines, and no contrary view is being stated here.) The dangers inherent in allowing the import of medicines from such unsuitable sources into the UK and their supply to the UK National Health Service was never an issue in this case. Instead, the case concerned itself with the more hygienic matters of the law on free trade and trademarks. The Court of Appeal concluded that, on the facts, the goods were first put on the market within the European Economic Area by GSK and not Dowelhurst because GSK sold and delivered the goods to France, not Africa. The court held that the GSK trademark rights were therefore 'exhausted' and that they had no fair complaint against Dowelhurst. GSK also tried to get an injunction to stop this happening again. The court decided that it should not grant an injunction on the basis that it is never possible to be sure about the past trading history of a given consignment of such goods and therefore an injunction would be a 'deterrent to legitimate trade'.

By definition, this decision is right in law. What it conceals is the issues of public importance which lie beneath the facts.

It should be said, in fairness to Dowelhurst, that they had done all they were legally required to do. They had ensured that the packaging was suitable for UK use and had advised the appropriate authorities that they were importing GSK's HIV/ Aids drugs. Of course, the very problem associated with parallel trade in medicine comes in part from the inability of the regulatory regime to cope with the huge quantities involved.

When goods arrive in the UK from abroad, packaged as intended by the manufacturer for sale abroad, the packaging and patient information inserts must be changed in order to comply with UK requirements. If the wording of the package does not comply with UK or European regulations, then the importer, if he has the appropriate licence, simply opens the package, inserts an English-language information leaflet, and adds or 'over-sticks' an English-language sticker or provides a new box with English-language details. If the importer does not have a licence then there are plenty who will repackage on a contractual basis. Otherwise, repackaging can be done abroad before export with the advantage to the illicit parallel trader that he is even better able to claim lack of 'guilty knowledge' should things go wrong.

Once repackaged, the products (120 million per annum) are ready for sale in the UK, perhaps straight to the NHS or to one or many more dealers who will add a further layer of anonymity, and a further profit, before they end up on the pharmacy shelf or in the hospital dispensary or GP surgery. Sometimes, in such circumstances, these medicines change hands 20 or 30 times before reaching the patient.[5] Why should NHS trusts, private hospitals, pharmacists, doctors and dentists buy goods that have passed through such hands? Two reasons seem apparent: they do not know their provenance, and they cost a little less.

According to research conducted by Liverpool University and published in July 2004, one in sixteen hospital admissions in the UK are now as a result of patients suffering an adverse reaction to medication. Researchers analysed the adverse drug reactions (ADRs) of a sample of 18,820 patients. The study, which was conducted from November 2001 to April 2002 in two NHS hospitals, revealed 1,225 admissions related to adverse drug reactions. These led to direct hospital admission in 80 per cent of cases. The projected annual cost to the NHS of such admissions is £466 million.[6] The study concluded that: 'the burden of ADRs on the NHS is high, accounting for consider-able morbidity, mortality, and extra costs', and that 'measures need to be put in place to reduce the burden of ADRs and thereby further improve the benefit:harm ratio of the drugs'.[7] As is often the case, the study does not mention the possible influence of counterfeit medicine. It does point out, however, that there has been little research into ADRs in the UK, and that what has been done has been on a small scale: 'In the United Kingdom, most studies were performed 10 to 30 years ago and were relatively small, often confined to individual units such as for care of the elderly. The largest UK study ... given the poor documentation ... probably underestimated the impact.'

The research suggests that in 2002 in England, ADRs caused the hospital admission, followed by the death, of 5,700 patients. The authors state: 'the true rate of death, taking into account all ADRs (those causing admission, and those occurring while patients are in hospital), may therefore turn out to be greater than 10,000 a year'.

The report also confirms that older drugs continue to be most commonly implicated in causing such admissions and deaths, and argues that 'measures are urgently needed to reduce the burden on the NHS'.[8]

It might be that none of these deaths or other adverse reactions is in any way attributable to the fact that many of these medicines may have been diverted from one part of the globe back to the UK, or may have passed through 20 to 30 different dealers in Europe. It may be that such well-travelled medicines are always in date at time of use and perfectly and accurately marked when repackaged, and never counterfeit. But it is impossible to find any means of logically concluding that we can be confident that this is the case.

Formal recording of incidents to assist in the prevention of adverse reaction to drugs was introduced following the thalido-mide disaster of the early 1970s, when regulations were insti-tuted to provide 'early warning' of any new medicine that was causing adverse reaction in patients. Since then more than 400,000 reports of suspected ADRs have been submitted by doctors, dentists, pharmacists, coroners, radiographers, optometrists and pharmaceutical companies under statutory obligations. This scheme, which is administered by the MHRA, is clearly vitally important to the health of UK citizens. It is known as the 'yellow card scheme' and requires a health professional to submit details of any adverse reaction to drugs to the MHRA. The scheme does not, however, require the 'health professional' to report the origin of the drugs or the name of the wholesaler or distributor who provided them. A source within the MHRA has said that within the last five years (although the MHRA have officially refuted this), not one enquiry has been passed from those at the MHRA responsible for receiving yellow cards (and entering details on to a database) to those within the same organisation responsible for investigating suspect activity. It also seems that, once details are entered on to the MHRA database, little more is done. All this means that if time-expired or counterfeit pharmaceuticals, or pharmaceuticals that have been stored at inappropriate temperatures or subject to temperature variations (for many need to be stored at a constant temperature), are being repackaged and consumed, then there is currently no effective mechanism for this to be discovered.

A major review of the yellow card scheme has just been concluded. This was chiefly carried out to consider whether the data collected should be made more widely available for analysis and research by others. According to the MHRA website, there are 'increasing numbers of requests by independent researchers in academia and clinical institutions, who wish to use the data for research and audit purposes, and ... the potential for new uses, e.g. in researching the use of genetics to reduce the burden of adverse drug reactions'. It is clearly in the public interest that suitably 'anonymised' information is made available for such purposes.

The MHRA website points out that 'The Yellow Card Scheme has been the cornerstone of monitoring drug safety for 40 years and has an excellent track record in protecting public health' and that the review was led by Dr Jeremy Metters, CB, a former Deputy Chief Medical Officer, supported by a steering committee of experts.

A review of the public and 'expert' views and opinions is being carried out at the time of writing, before the review findings are published. It is said that twenty-four important recommendations will be made for change, which will allow greater access to the data generated by the yellow card scheme to ensure that the full potential of the data is realised. Significantly, the amended scheme will still not ask the person reporting the adverse reaction to identify from which wholesaler the product was purchased, or seek to establish if it was a parallel-traded item. Nor does the scheme ask any specific questions to assist in the identification of counterfeiting trends.

The review group states that the scheme 'has a proven track record of identifying new drug safety hazards and is recognised to be one of the best in the world in terms of the level of reporting' (see the website referred to above). It should be noted, however, that 'identifying new drug safety hazards' is not the same as identifying new safety hazards with drugs. The yellow card scheme looks primarily for difficulties with new drugs, new pharmaceuticals and new products, and not with those pharmaceuticals that are well established. Yet it is, of course, on these established drugs – these best-sellers – that the counterfeiters and others with disreputable motives concentrate their efforts, and it is these drugs which account for a disturbing number of admissions to hospital following an adverse drug reaction.

We have recently seen the formation in the UK of the National Patient Safety Agency. This is dedicated to reducing the harm done to patients by medicines and their administration. Its website states: 'The National Patient Safety Agency (NPSA) is a Special Health Authority created to co-ordinate the efforts of all those involved in healthcare, and more importantly to learn from patient safety incidents occurring in the NHS.'[9]

The NPSA Corporate Plan (2003–04) states in its introduction that the NPSA was created 'To set up a national reporting and learning system for staff and patients to tell us about adverse incidents *and their root causes* and most importantly to use the information collected to develop practical solutions to improve patient safety for all.'[10]

The information is collected by electronic questionnaire. This questionnaire, which those reporting ADRs are requested to complete, is comprehensive, and questions are asked that have the potential to identify problems arising from parallel-traded pharmaceuticals. This is a major step forward. Such questions (and issues) include:

➤ Wrong/omitted/passed expiry date

➤ Wrong/omitted patient information leaflet

➤ Wrong/transposed/omitted medicine label

➤ Wrong/unclear dose or strength

➤ Wrong drug/medicine

➤ Wrong formulation

➤ Wrong frequency

➤ Wrong method of preparation/supply

➤ Wrong quantity

➤ Medicines with similar-looking or sounding names

➤ Poor labelling and packaging from a commercial
manufacturer
Manufacturer:
Batch number:

➤ Is the medicine a manufactured special?

➤ Has the medicine been purchased from a registered
EU importer and relabelled for the UK market (parallel
import)?
Serial number:
Manufacturer:
Supplier:
Batch number:
Expiry date:

The agency admits that there are no questions designed to
identify counterfeit medicines, and it is true that further specific
questions might have been included, but this questionnaire, if
it is routinely and fully completed, will nonetheless provide a
database that, if skilfully searched, will supply useful leads in
assisting a proper evaluation of the extent of this problem.

The overall description of the NPSA's role and purpose

indicates a duty in the prevention of counterfeit and 'out of date' medicines reaching UK patients. What stronger 'root cause' could there be of adverse drug reactions? It would obviously be shallow to assume that the 'audit trail' on adverse reactions to medicines begins with a conclusion that the pharmaceutical product administered is, in all respects, what it purports to be.

The NPSA say: 'With an estimated 850,000 incidents either harming or nearly harming an NHS hospital inpatient in the UK each year, reducing medical errors and improving patient safety are critical issues in healthcare today.' So they are, and account must now be taken of the effect of the global trade in pharmaceuticals and the dangers reflected in the practice of parallel trading and product repackaging.

The NPSA have formed a modern searchable database that takes comprehensive data from a range of sources in order to provide information to serve their purposes. As yet they have not had the opportunity to become fully conversant with the potential of their new database and information collection processes. It has become clear during this research that the NPSA has not yet fully explored the threat of counterfeit medicines, yet they clearly have the tools and the remit to contribute much.

It is still the case that the NPSA can say: 'counterfeit medicines are monitored and the responsibility of the MHRA. The issue of out of date medicines is the responsibility of the Royal Pharmaceutical Society and the MHRA. The NPSA does not have active work strands on either issue as it would duplicate what other Agencies are already doing'.[11] It is not in the public interest for the NPSA to leave it at that.

There is currently no link between the database being developed by the NPSA and that maintained by the MHRA.

5

Opportunities in an under-policed environment

What are the prospects for enhanced police or law enforcement activity in this environment? According to the Audit Commision (2001) and the Department of Health (2000):

➤ Medication errors account for 11 per cent of hospital admissions in the UK. There are about 850,000 adverse events every year, with an average of 7–8.4 bed days per adverse event.

➤ There is an extra annual expenditure of £1.1 billion on drug-related adverse events, up to 70 per cent of which are preventable.

➤ 95 per cent of problems are due to 'processes', and only 5 per cent to people.[1]

Parallel trading is in essence an international distribution chain sometimes taken advantage of by unscrupulous businessmen. Counterfeiting is the manufacture of illicit products in need of international distribution chains run by unscrupulous businessmen. This is the essential and logical link between these two activities.

There is no even remotely adequate market testing for counterfeit medicines in the UK. There have, however, been a number of criminal cases involving counterfeit pharmaceuticals over the last few years, both in the UK and more broadly in Europe. Nevertheless, no official statistics are kept by any agency. Every case identified has been as a result of an agency (police, trading standards, MHRA, rights holder, Customs and Excise) simply tripping over suspicious activity. None has been a result of proactivity, target prioritisation, analysis of suspicious trends or collation of criminal intelligence.

When it comes to dealing with crime matters and identifying significant problems, then two sorts of crime need to be identified. There are those sorts where the victim will normally report the crime, or have it reported on their behalf – burglary, robbery, car theft, murder, etc. – and those where no report is usually made – drug importation, dealing in child pornography, white-collar crime. These crimes, important as each is, usually need to be looked for if they are to be found. They are sometimes wrongly called 'victimless crimes' on the basis that the victim does not usually make a complaint (or report). Counterfeiting of medicines, and selling out-of-date or otherwise dangerous pharmaceuticals, is in this latter category – and no one is looking to establish the extent of these offences on our behalf. As the head of Interpol, Ron Noble, has recently pointed out, 'Law enforcement agencies have to recognize that Intellectual Property Crime is not a victimless crime … it must be seen as a very serious crime with important implications for public safety and security.'[2]

Indeed, the normal reaction of the law enforcement agencies and the nature of the Home Office crime reporting system combine to conceal the true extent of these crimes.

The typical reaction of the police, in the unlikely event that they agree to accept a counterfeiting investigation, is to prefer or insist that any criminal charges should be shown as contrary to the Theft Act (obtaining property by deception) or contrary to legislation designed to deal with prohibited drugs (heroin, cannabis, amphetamines, anabolic steroids, etc.) rather than the Trade Marks Act or other tailor-made legislation. This is understandable: the maximum penalty for criminal deception is ten years' imprisonment, the same as for the counterfeiting of branded goods. This cannot be said for the prohibition on the manufacture and sale of class C drugs (steroids, etc.), which the police have used instead of the Trade Marks Act. Not only can the penalties be similar but the police understand and are familiar with their powers and 'the points to prove' under a Theft Act charge – not so when it comes to trademark charges.

Yet charging offenders under the Theft Act or drugs legislation has the effect of burying the offences in a way that makes each case invisible to the Home Office or any crime researcher. Prosecutions for counterfeiting of pharmaceuticals in the Home Office crime statistics are subsumed into the categories 'fraud, other', 'forgery' or those relating to drugs offences. There is no method of searching national police statistics to identify the extent of pharmaceuticals counterfeiting.

The MHRA has legal powers to enforce regulations made under the Medicines Act. There is no offence of counterfeiting medicines created by this act, however. This means that currently the MHRA has to prosecute for lesser offences under the act or attempt to involve other agencies, e.g. the police, who are reluctant to pursue cases under the Trade Marks Act or other intellectual property legislation. This further obfuscates the true position.

6

Linking 'diversion', parallel trade and counterfeiting

The recent US case involving the recall of 60 million Lipitor tablets (a mix of counterfeited and diverted products) has already been referred to. Diversion and parallel trade often necessarily involve repackaging. The WHO, when discussing the many deaths that have resulted from counterfeit and substandard medicines, clearly identifies the dangers that come from repackaging. It states: 'Because of a lack of regulation and enforcement, the quality, safety and efficacy of both imported and locally manufactured medicines in many developing countries cannot be guaranteed. Subsequently, smuggling and illegal importation of drugs are often rife. Substandard and counterfeit drugs are then not only sold in these countries but also exported or re-exported.'[1] This is an important point – it is wrong to assume, when goods can easily be offered for sale from the remotest places, that export from poorer countries of the world to Europe will not take place.

The situation is worsened by the fact that medicines exported from many industrialised countries are not regulated to the same level as those domestically consumed, while export of drugs to developing countries via free trade zones is increasing. Re-labelling of products to mask details of their origin is also known to occur.

The WHO factsheet points out that 'some policymakers now believe that drug regulation represents an unnecessary barrier to trade and should be reduced to a minimum. Pharmaceuticals, however, cannot be considered a standard commodity since consumers and prescribers are unable to assess their quality, safety and efficacy and the results can be harmful to patients' health'.[2]

7

The growth in illicit trade and counterfeiting

Illicit trade in pharmaceuticals is clearly a growth industry around the world. The executive summary of the US Food and Drug Administration (FDA) report *Combating Counterfeit Drugs* says: 'In recent years ... the FDA has seen growing evidence of efforts by increasingly well-organised counterfeiters backed by increasingly sophisticated technologies and criminal operations to profit from drug counterfeiting at the expense of American patients.'[1] The report makes clear that it does not assess the USA as being alone among industrialised countries in facing this threat. This is reflected in the number of nations that attended a two-day conference for drug regulators held in Madrid in 2004. Although they concluded that further discussions would be needed before a global treaty could be signed, they accepted that the growing trade in pharmaceutical counterfeits results in death, disability and injury.[2]

It is, of course, the richer countries which spend most on medicines, and because of their wealth they are the most attractive targets for diversion. As the poorest countries develop, so will their ability to buy drugs, and so will their ability to both divert drugs and manufacture them illicitly. As the pharmaceuticals market expands, so will diversion and counterfeiting.

The WHO estimates that counterfeits comprise more than 10 per cent of the global market in medicines, and are present in both industrialised and developing countries.[3] These statistics have been adopted by the United States FDA, although there has been little comment on this by health authorities within Europe or by pharmaceutical companies themselves.

There are many estimates as to the value of the counterfeit drug market, but there is no standard way of assessing it. Often values are based on manufacturing cost without reference to the tax evasion (wholesale cost) that results, or the cost of the spread of disease that useless drugs facilitate. Other costs, such as those of subsequent remedial treatment, remain unevaluated. A recent *Independent on Sunday* special investigation claimed that the global counterfeit drug industry is worth around £20 billion, which is in line with UN WHO estimates.[4]

While western Europe has been largely blind to the counterfeiting of medicines, the situation in other parts of Europe is rather different. Recent research suggests that 10 per cent of the pharmaceuticals in the distribution chain in Russia are counterfeit.[5] The WHO has rightly pointed to the dangers of Russian counterfeits and is also aware that Russia is a major supply route for counterfeit pharmaceuticals originating in countries such as India and China. European Union enlargement radically increases the border with Russia and makes importation of Russian products easier.[6]

The EU accession countries are significantly poorer than the older members and have well-established trading ties with

Russia. The outcome in terms of motivation, temptation and opportunity is obvious.

The opportunities for countries such as Poland are not lost on them. Already Poland, like others, is trading strongly with China and India, two of the largest manufacturers of fake drugs. The Polish authorities are pushing to encourage direct trade with these countries. Poland, the largest country in central Europe, ranks eighth in Europe by size of population and ninth by area. It was the first country in central and eastern Europe to make the transition to a market economy. Foreign trade grew from US$14.9 billion in 1989 to $96.1 billion in 2002. Exports have been that country's economic driving force, and India and China have played a significant part. China's share in Poland's imports has risen to 3.8 per cent, making it one of the ten largest exporting countries to Poland. As an illustration of the extent to which China is a cause of potential problems, in 2003 the State Drug Administration closed 1,300 illegal factories in China and investigated cases of counterfeit drugs worth $57 million.[7]

India and Poland have had extensive bilateral trading arrangements for over sixty years. These have recently been further cemented with an exchange of high-level visits, including the visit in 2003 of Poland's premier, Leszek Miller, to India. This visit incorporated extensive business delegations. Between 2000 and 2003, India increased its exports to Poland from US$140 million to US$180 million.[8]

Exports from India to Poland more than doubled between 1992 and 2002. It is estimated that such trade will continue to expand as fresh opportunities open up for sales into wider Europe. The figures are likely to touch US$225 million in 2003.[9] It seems that India's export basket to Poland is fairly diversified.

'Our major exports have been bulk tea, coffee, unmanufactured tobacco ... pharmaceutical and chemical ... light engineering products etc.'[10] On entry into the EU in 2004, Poland adopted the EU's common customs tariff, which is likely to benefit imports from India. Presently, there are no restrictions or quotas on imports from India.

A quick search of the Internet (July 2004) quickly revealed Polish commercial offerings such as the following, which is the actual text as it appears:

We do Parallel Trading with branded:
- pharmaceuticals (from GSK, Pfizer, Astra-Zeneca, Novartis, Aventis, Roche, Bayer, and many other companies)
- blood diagnostics (from Medisense/Abbot, Bayer, Lifescan/Johnson&Johnson, Roche, Menarini)
- medical materials (from ConvaTec, Johnson&Johnson, 3M, Smith+Nephew, Coloplast, Bard, Lohmann & Rauscher, Moelnycke, BD, Kimberly-Clark, Paperpack and other)
- dental materials (from 3M, ESPE, Vivadent, Heraeus-Kulzer, Agfa Dental, Kodak and other)
- medical x-ray films (Kodak, Agfa, Fuji)
- surgical products (Portex, Ethicon, Sherwood, Hudson and other)
- medical equipment (OMRON)
- OTC products (DUREX, RFSU)
- optical products (Baush & Lomb, Allergan)

It may of course be that the persons behind this particular website are perfectly legitimate, that they have no involvement with counterfeit products easily available from Russia, China or India, and that the stock they are exporting to other parts of Europe is properly stored and moved quickly in proper conditions so that shelf-life is not significantly shortened.

For many years, China did little to curb the amount of counterfeiting that took place within its borders. Investigators in the Far East would tell of experiences that clearly indicated that the authorities at best turned a blind eye to such activity. It is as a result of US political pressure that China has in the last four years wanted to be perceived as taking intellectual property rights seriously. Thus Xinhuanet.com reported in May 2004 that the director of the Chinese State Food and Drug Agency, Zheng Xiaoyu, claimed that 994 pharmaceutical counterfeiting manufacturing facilities had been closed down during 2003, with the seizure of US$60 million worth of fake pharmaceuticals. Perhaps this gives some idea of the scale of the problem in China alone.

An approach by the author to one Internet business site in August 2004, to enter negotiations with a named Polish company, listed as being able to supply pharmaceuticals in commercial quantities within Europe, was answered by a Chinese manufacturer keen to share his catalogue of Chinese-manufactured pharmaceuticals.

The WHO factsheet on *Counterfeit and Substandard Medicines* states that: 'The United States Food and Drug Administration estimates that counterfeits make up more than 10% of the global medicines market and are present in both industrialised and developing countries.'[11] A WHO survey of counterfeit medicine reports from twenty countries between January 1999 and October 2000 found that 60 per cent of counterfeit medicine cases occurred in poor countries and 40 per cent in industrialised countries.[12]

Which types of drug are the target of counterfeiters? It is well known that Viagra and other erectile dysfunction drugs are widely circulated via the Internet. These, along with body-building steroids and slimming tablets, are often thought of as 'lifestyle drugs' and as being the target for counterfeiters. Each is certainly counterfeited, and counterfeit Viagra is on sale in public houses as frequently as steroids in some gymnasiums. To conclude that these lifestyle drugs pose the chief counterfeiting problem, however, would be to dangerously misunderstand the nature of the problem.

Malaria is a global killer on a massive scale. Malarial drugs are frequently counterfeited, and the counterfeit products and packaging, even to the expert eye, are extremely difficult to detect. A recent study in *The Lancet* concluded that up to 40 per cent of artusenate products (for the treatment of malaria) contain no active ingredients. It is impossible to know how many deaths have resulted but one study stated that '200,000 would be avoidable (annually) if the medicines available were effective, of good quality and used correctly'.

There have been many thousands of deaths worldwide resulting from pharmaceutical counterfeiting. A few further examples follow:

➤ The Anti-Counterfeiting Group (ACG), a brand-owners' organisation, report on their website that: 'In China the state-controlled *Shenzhen Evening News* reported that 192,000 people died in China as a result of fake drugs in 2001.'[13]

➤ The consumption of paracetamol cough syrup prepared with diethylene glycol (a toxic chemical used in antifreeze) led to 89 deaths in Haiti in 1995 and 30 infant deaths in India in 1998.

➤ The website of the Alliance Against Counterfeiting and Piracy announces: 'Fake Vaccines Lead to 3,000 Deaths'. Following reports of a meningitis epidemic in Niger, the international community responded in September 1997 by sending vaccine. One such shipment, comprising 68,000 doses, was sent to Nigeria via the WHO. There, it appears to have been counterfeited. Later tests by the manufacturer, Merieux, confirmed that the substitute 'vaccine' had no active ingredients. Three thousand deaths are thought to have resulted.[14]

8

Case studies

Although the central point of this book is that the UK and European citizen might currently be consuming counterfeit and otherwise substandard medicines, and suffering as a result, we simply cannot know to what extent. We can assess the likelihood, however, by looking at what is happening in the rest of the world, and in particular at societies that in relevant ways mirror our own. For an example of what is occurring in a country that can afford to pay relatively highly for its pharmaceuticals, it is useful to look at the USA. Several cases that have recently been discovered there are reported in the Appendix, though others are mentioned in passing, as and when relevant.

It is currently impossible to identify in any straightforward way the number of counterfeiting incidents that have been occurring in Europe, and thereby establish what injury might be the result. The difficulty arises because no regulatory authority is watching out, no public intelligence system is collating the facts, public records fail to reveal details of significant incidents, and the extent of these crimes remains concealed. Despite this, it has been possible to gain information from two sources on particular cases. The first source is confidential, as a result of which it can be stated that there are currently three separate significant pharmaceutical counterfeiting investigations ongoing in the UK in August 2004. One involves the alleged mass production in Britain of several well-known branded pharmaceuticals. The second concerns the UK and Europe being used as a market for very large commercial quantities of many counterfeit pharmaceuticals that have been manufactured elsewhere. The third involves large quantities of a well-known counterfeit pharmaceutical product being found by an innocent agent in the UK. Such cases should result in counterfeiting charges and significant press coverage, but if history is anything to go by this is by no means certain.

The other source is public. The following cases are all a matter of record. This short list is not comprehensive, but simply represents those cases that are known to the author. All have been discovered by the authorities by accident; none has been detected as a result of any proactivity. How could they have been? No one is looking.

1 In 2003, a dealer in Kent bought a consignment of Aids drugs from a dealer in Essex. The Essex dealer, when raided, had incriminating documents plus half a tonne of cannabis on the premises. Police dropped the cannabis charges when the dealer claimed that he knew nothing about it! Some of the Aids drugs, which had circulated the world before coming back into the UK as parallel-traded items and being stored with cannabis in Essex, were being sold by the dealer to NHS hospitals.

2   In 1998, counterfeit Losec was parallel-imported and spotted by the parallel importer as not appearing genuine. Some 6,000 bottles had been bought from a licensed dealer in Italy.

3   In 1999, Eli Lilly goods were delivered to Preston, Lancashire, and supplied to a patient, who found that they had been damaged in transit and sent the damaged goods directly to Eli Lilly to complain. On examination by Lilly they were found to be part of a larger consignment intended for the Red Cross in Russia. The Russian mafia was believed to be involved.

4   In 1994, a UK wholesaler found that 'good quality' counterfeit Zantac (a GlaxoSmithKline product) had been delivered to him in the UK from Greece. This was the fourth occasion on which this product had been seen in Britain.

5   In 2001, counterfeit Viagra tablets were discovered in Oldham. These had originated in Thailand. The offender was bailed and absconded.

6   In the mid-1990s, counterfeit Losec was discovered being distributed in North London.

7   In 2000, counterfeit Nubain – an injectable painkiller – was being counterfeited in Newcastle by an offender who was sentenced to five years' imprisonment for criminal deception.

8   In the late 1990s, Humatrope, an Eli Lilly product, was being illegally manufactured in a factory at Pilling near Liverpool. The offender was sentenced to five years, though he maintained that he was forced to manufacture this

product having been subject to assault and death threats by a Liverpool crime gang.

9 Counterfeit Dermovate was seen in many London pharmacies in the 1990s. Cynically advertised by the counterfeiters as a product that would 'lighten the skin', it contained steroids that could cause permanent damage to sensitive skin areas on the face.

9

Organised crime and terrorism

The term 'organised crime' may conjure up the traditional caricature of dark-suited Italian and Italian-American armed gangsters. The reality, however, has more to do with intelligent, determined and unscrupulous individuals wherever they are in the world (London, Beijing or Basingstoke) acting together and prepared to invest money and time in any illegal venture that will maximise profit. This is a more accurate description of modern organised crime, and perhaps reflects precise descriptions of successful organised crime over the last twenty years. It is simply not sensible to expose oneself or one's business by taking part in overtly anti-social, high-visibility crime when there are ways of avoiding the attention of the authorities.

It is this more sophisticated understanding of 'organised crime', reflecting the type of crime and criminality that poses a real threat to UK citizens, which is behind Britain's National Criminal Intelligence Service (NCIS) definition.[1] NCIS provides annually a description of the main threats to this country from 'organised crime', defining not only this term but also 'serious crime', for NCIS is concerned with organised crime's involvement in 'serious crime'.

Serious crime is defined as offences where 'a person aged 21 or over on first conviction could expect to be imprisoned for three or more years'. Counterfeiting of branded products is punishable with ten years' imprisonment on indictment. When the purchaser is fooled into believing they are the real thing – and therefore the offence of criminal deception is involved – the penalty on indictment is ten years. Should the counterfeit product cause foreseeable harm to the user, and the user suffer serious injury or death, the maximum penalty is life imprisonment. Clearly, counterfeiting of pharmaceuticals is serious crime as defined by NCIS.

The NCIS report, in providing a rationale for the prioritisation of the work of the agency, describes those crimes that are 'the work of serious and organised criminals (those involved, normally working with others, in continuing serious criminal activities for substantial profit or gain, whether based in the UK or elsewhere)'.

It goes on (para. 1.4):

Just as not all serious or organised crimes are relevant [to the NCIS threat assessment] not all serious and organised criminal activity that is relevant is carried out by cadre members of organised crime groups. For organised crime groups to thrive, their activities require not only organisation in the sense of planning but also to be supported by some form of criminal or quasi-legitimate infrastructure. For example, throughout the UK there are drugs distributors and dealers who are critical to the criminal businesses of organised trafficking groups but who do not belong to any particular group. Though these individuals may associate with, buy from and even pay a percentage of their profits to an organised crime group, they operate essentially for and by themselves. Perhaps less obviously, serious and organised criminals rely not only on other criminals but also on professionals, such as solicitors, accountants and businessmen, whom they draw into their criminal enterprises to facilitate and protect them, and launder their criminal profits.

These, as well as law-abiding pharmacists, doctors and other health professionals, can be the unknowing agents of this illicit trade.

The 2002 annual NCIS report states:

in producing [the report], NCIS looks across the range of serious and organised criminal activity [and] ... the Home Office-chaired Strategic Customer Group (a sub-group of the Organised Crime Strategy Group), consisting of senior representatives from those government departments and agencies most closely concerned with tackling serious and organised crime, considers the most significant threats facing the UK to be:

- ➤ Class A drugs trafficking (heroin, cocaine powder, crack cocaine and ecstasy)
- ➤ organised immigration crime
- ➤ fraud (particularly revenue fraud)
- ➤ money laundering
- ➤ (possession and use of) firearms

➤ hi-tech crime
➤ sex offences against children, including online child abuse

The list is not in priority order.

The report goes on to give a general outline of each of these seven crime areas. Under 'hi-tech crime' it says (para. 8.1):

> With the development and spread of digital technology, intellectual property crime offers potentially lucrative opportunities for serious and organised criminals. ... Technical know-how is required to crack the security features, but thereafter production and distribution calls for largely non-technical criminal methods and infrastructures. Distribution may involve traditional forms of smuggling. However, pirated goods are increasingly marketed and distributed via the internet. ... the ready consumer market for pirated goods, low chance of detection and low penalties attracted by such offences following conviction all serve to make intellectual property crime attractive to organised criminal groups.

The 2003 NCIS threat assessment says (para. 1.35):

> Intellectual property crime is taking place on a vast scale globally. Advances in technology have facilitated its growth, by enabling the speedy reproduction of high quality counterfeit goods, the best of which are difficult to differentiate from the genuine articles. The counterfeiting of CDs, DVDs and other digital media, much of it done in the Far East, is well-publicised, but

the counterfeiting of all types of goods from designer clothes to pharmaceuticals is also rife. Many serious and organised criminals are involved, either in the manufacture of counterfeit products, or in their distribution, attracted by the high profits and the low risk of detection, and no doubt conscious of the fact that the penalties for intellectual property crime offences are rarely more than minimal. Meanwhile, there remains a public perception of intellectual property crime as a victimless crime, despite the fact that certain counterfeit products, such as car or aircraft parts, pharmaceuticals and alcohol, pose a direct risk to the public. Where serious and organised criminals are involved, it is reasonable to assume that a proportion of the profits is used to fund other serious crimes.

At para 2.1 it states:

When deciding what crimes to commit, and how, where, when and with whom to go about them, serious and organised criminals are guided by considerations of profit, risk, opportunity and capability. The vast majority of serious and organised criminal activity is directly or indirectly concerned with making money. The criminals look to do so without getting caught, and therefore they manage risk. The decisions they make involve a balancing of anticipated profit and risk, but also rely on identifying an opportunity and having the capability to exploit it.

The report continues at para. 3.7:

Although most of the largest importers of heroin and cocaine tend to concentrate on one or other drug, many drugs traffickers appear largely unconcerned about the different types of drugs they handle and, by inference, the different penalties they face should they be caught. The pattern of poly-drug use provides an obvious incentive for traffickers to engage in multi-drug trafficking, rather than limiting themselves to one commodity. The key concerns are opportunity, capability, and profit. Therefore, if they have access to them, can handle the logistics of importation, and can buy and sell at a profit, some smugglers of Class A drugs will readily smuggle cannabis (which remains the most widely used drug in the UK), amphetamine (the market for which appears to be in decline) or pharmaceuticals (such as Viagra and its various copies, the market for which is strong), importing the drugs in 'cocktail' loads or consecutively.

The WHO factsheet reiterates the point:

Counterfeiting of medicines is a hugely lucrative business due to high demand and low production costs. The absence of deterrent legislation in many countries also encourages counterfeiters since there is no fear of being apprehended and prosecuted. When prices of medicines are high and price differentials between identical products exist there is a greater incentive for the consumer to seek medicines outside the normal supply system.[2]

When counterfeit or diverted products of whatever type (jeans, beans or machines) are sold, the financial benefit goes to those who organise the crime – often organised crime and sometimes terrorist organisations. The result is that:

➤ Danger is sometimes caused to the consumer (with pharmaceuticals, other health products, foodstuffs, machine parts, e.g. car brake-pads, aeroplane engine parts, etc.).

➤ The ill-gotten gains are used to fund other crimes of a conventional or terrorist nature – and further public harm is done.

➤ Companies that are heavily reliant on research and development for their survival (pharmaceutical companies in particular) are starved of revenue by those who have no need to invest in R&D.

➤ Tax evasion by the criminals results in tax loss to the Exchequer – which logically implies that everyone else pays more tax.

As if all that were not enough, it must be apparent that once a connection to terrorism is shown the potential to inflict massive injury is clear. What more simple method could there be for the terrorist to cause massive loss of life than simply introducing a noxious substance into our most frequently used drugs, or conducting germ warfare by intro-ducing an agent via a counterfeit, injectable pharmaceutical product?

Any known involvement of terrorist organisations in the counterfeiting of pharmaceuticals should therefore be a strong signal to governments that reasonable protective measures should be put in place. Usually, but by no means invariably, the link from pharmaceutical counterfeiting to terrorism is via organised crime.

Several cases 'accidentally' uncovered within the UK have already been described in brief; two of these could fairly be described as 'organised crime' cases. Other European countries face similar problems; some have clearly identified the threat. In Italy, for example, it is known that Italian criminal groups that maintain global cells and associations are involved in illegal activity within the pharmaceutical domain.

In 1995, an investigation that detected the involvement of the Naples-based organised crime group, the Camorra, uncovered a clandestine facility used to manufacture counterfeit pharmaceuticals.

In 2000, approximately 250,000 doses and two tons of raw material (valued at US$1 million) originating from India and China were seized during another investigation into organised crime. The goods were being repackaged in Europe for resale in the Americas.[3]

The Italian government has disclosed that links between Islamic terrorist groups and the Camorra have been since identified.[4]

In 2003, Lavinia Carey, chair of the trade group Alliance Against Counterfeiting and Piracy, published a report, *Proving the Connection*, which stated:

> Ever since the Alliance officially launched in the Summer of 1999, announcing £6.4 billion lost to the UK economy through counterfeiting and piracy, we have made references to links between intellectual property

(IP) theft and organised crime. Although anecdotal, we knew that these links existed because of the evidence which our members' anti-piracy units were turning up in the course of enforcing the intellectual property rights (IPR) within their industries.[5]

She continues:

Previously, there may have been a suspicion among statutory law enforcement agencies that a degree of imprecision exists among IPR agencies applying the term organised crime. But the same can be said of police, customs and other enforcement agencies that have yet to identify with the extent of the problem. The growth in IPR fraud which is reported by The Alliance is attributed by Alliance members to ease of offending, huge profits and lack of credible sanctions.

This issue has recently been the subject of debate in Brussels under the chair of the Directorate General of Internal Justice and Affairs, who is leading a forum for the prevention of organised crime. It has declared:

The greater involvement of criminal organisations and sometimes even of terrorist groups in major international trafficking of counterfeits and pirated goods is evidence of the particularly lucrative nature of these activities and of the increased sophistication of methods of fraud. This new threat, because of its scale, requires the setting up of new instruments within the Union and new techniques to detect fraud.

Lavinia Carey also quotes the relatively new Interpol Intellectual Property Group, which says that 'extensive evidence is now available from the public and private sectors which demonstrates that organised criminals and terrorists are heavily involved in planning and committing these [IPR] crimes'.[6]

At the International Conference of Drug Regulatory Authorities (ICDRA), regulators from some forty countries met in Madrid early in 2004 to discuss the growing extent of counterfeit pharmaceuticals and to plan wider international cooperation. A 'concept paper' on a proposed international framework was presented by the WHO.[7] It was said that the number of cases investigated by the United States FDA rose from six in 1997 to 22 in 2002. Leaving aside the huge underreporting of these crimes, what should be made clear is that 22 cases do not represent 22 boxes of medicines. Each and any one of them can represent a danger to thousands of lives. One case, for example, which is mentioned elsewhere in this paper, concerned 60 million tablets that had been counterfeited and sold through the legitimate distribution chain in the USA.

Erik Madsen of Interpol told the ICDRA meeting that emerging evidence shows that counterfeiting has been linked to organised crime and terrorist organisations, including al-Qaeda.[8] This statement from an Interpol staff member is not an isolated conclusion. John Therriou, vice-president of the pharmaceutical company Pfizer, made a similar statement in London during 2004 concerning similar links.

The Madrid conference rightly pointed to the need both for countries to establish laws to strengthen necessary regulation and legislation and for countries to work together to solve this global problem. This will mean active cooperation and concerted efforts by drug regulators, law enforcement agencies and members of the drugs industry.

At the moment each of those important stakeholders can turn a blind eye when these problems, potential and actual, are pointed out. Individuals in these agencies have been known to say, 'Show me the bodies', 'Show me the proof'. The truth is that while not enough hard data is available to establish an accurate picture, there is surely enough of the picture available for responsible decision-makers to make an effort to clarify things.

At the Madrid conference, Dr Lembit Rago, the WHO's coordinator of quality assurance and safety of medicines, suggested that the pharmaceutical companies were being secretive. This appears to be true, although there are exceptions.[9] It is certainly sufficiently true for governments to take note and to encourage greater openness.

The reporting systems whereby incidents of counterfeiting enter the WHO official figures vary from country to country. There is a general onus on national agencies to report cases, yet the WHO figures clearly indicate vast under-reporting. The WHO representative at the Madrid conference said that WHO had received no incident reports of counterfeit drugs from member countries since 2002, and only 84 reports between 1999 and 2002.[10] These figures are incredible to anyone who has been at all involved in countering this problem. It is certain, and within the author's knowledge, that many individual pharmaceutical companies have received numerous reports over the last two years of serious, life-threatening incidents of pharmaceutical counterfeiting. The United States FDA statistics alone belie the WHO figures. And the USA comes way down any sensible list of countries in which counterfeit products have been found.

In the mid-1990s, when the author set up the Counterfeiting of Branded Goods Sub-group under the auspices of the Metropolitan Police-chaired Joint Action Group, the (then) Royal Ulster Constabulary were one of the first invitees. Even then they had concluded that there was an established link between counterfeiting of branded products and terrorism. The lead group on this subject within the RUC was the Anti-Racketeering Unit. It was no surprise, then, that in its 2002 threat assessment the Police Service of Northern Ireland's (PSNI) Organised Crime Task Force reported that 'IPT [intellectual property theft] is a major local problem and there are close links with organised crime and the paramilitaries'.

It is known to the author that counterfeit goods to the value of £6.7 million were seized by PSNI in 2002, compared with £4 million in 2001. These were not pharmaceuticals. The PSNI, however, are known to be the most active police service in these islands when it comes to IPR crime. Other police forces are simply not generally looking.

In 2004 the head of Interpol gave public testimony to the effect that 'Terrorist financing is the generation of funds via licit or illicit means that are then remitted to a terrorist organisation or its front organisation via formal or informal financial channels.' His evidence used information held in files at Interpol from Interpol member states, trade bodies, manufacturers and rights holders, and a range of open sources. He assessed the global trade in counterfeit goods at US$ 450 billion. Generally, he said, it is organised and controlled by criminals or criminal organisations. The report of his evidence continues: 'Funds given to terrorist organisations have diverse origins. Licit and illicit activities can be used to generate funds. Licit origins can include donations from sympathisers or legitimate enterprises owned by terrorist organisations.'

On the specific links between counterfeiting of branded goods and terrorist financing, Mr Noble reported: 'The link between organised crime groups and counterfeit goods is well established. But Interpol is sounding the alarm that Intellectual Property Crime is becoming the preferred method of funding for a number of terrorist groups'.

He continued: '… because of the growing evidence that terrorist groups sometimes fund their activities using the proceeds, it must be seen as a very serious crime with important implications for public safety and security'.

Later in the Interpol report, specific examples are provided of counterfeiting and terrorist financing. They include reference to loyalist and Unionist terrorists in Northern Ireland; Kosovo, where 'there is a long-standing relationship between criminal organisations and local ethnic-Albanian extremist groups'; Chechen separatists – in 2000 'Chechen organised crime groups and terrorist organisations were benefiting from counterfeit good manufacturing and trafficking. A number of explosives and arms were also confiscated by the police during raids on the residences of the suspects'; North Africa, where radical fundamentalist terrorists were involved; Europe, where 'Interpol possesses information that indicates that sympathisers of radical fundamentalists may be involved via the method of charitable giving in Islam (zakat)'. More exactly, Ron Noble specified that: 'A militant active in Europe, known for his activities in radical fundamentalist organisations over the last decade, has been recently convicted for trafficking in counterfeit goods. The individual's counterfeiting associates are also known members of radical fundamentalist groups. They are reported as still being involved in large-scale counterfeit goods trafficking.'

Noble stated that one counterfeiting case has been reported as having connections to al-Qaeda. Furthermore, Interpol are apparently aware of three cases of counterfeiting activity involving Hezbollah terrorist funding in South America. These cases involve ethnic Lebanese who are involved in the remittance of funds to Hezbollah.

10

Conclusions and recommendations

C urrently, in the UK and Europe more widely, there is a lack of understanding, a lack of sufficient dedicated resources, a lack of information and communication – and perhaps some wilful blindness – on the issue of the nature and extent of the trade in dangerous pharmaceuticals. This environment provides both a threat to general safety and ongoing opportunities for unscrupulous businessmen and organised crime and terrorism. Much can be done to increase patient safety and to diminish the opportunity for crime and deceit to flourish.

To make the most of current opportunities, and to be most effective and economical, any UK strategy must take advantage of current good work, recognise the different but equally valuable roles that each agency can play, involve both the public and the private sector, look across Europe and coordinate efforts with like-minded interests, and then look wider still to embrace efforts on other continents and multi-national initiatives.

One of the most important initiatives that has the potential to link the pharmaceutical industry to public authority efforts is that started in 2004 by the UK Patent Office. This initiative, to form an Intellectual Property Crime Group, will seek to receive and collate information on counterfeiting from across industry and share it as appropriate with public authorities – regulatory, law enforcement and intelligence communities. Just how great their resources will be is yet to be established, and their working practices and style have yet to be witnessed. This is, however, a great opportunity and a much-needed step on the part of the UK Patent Office. The Patent Office Enforcement Strategy, published in August 2004, which seeks to unite domestic law enforcement and commercial efforts and relate the results to the international scene, is also bold, challenging and much needed.

It has been several years since I published a draft strategy at the UK Anti-Counterfeiting Group Conference. It has evolved since and is reproduced in outline here. It forms a three-pronged strategy.

Education

As long as governments, prosecutors, the judiciary, law enforcement officials, health regulators, manufacturers, parallel traders, pharmacists, NHS purchasing agents, the media and the public remain unaware of the nature and scale of the threat from counterfeit and substandard medicines, then inadequate legislation, inappropriate charges, inappropriate sentences, lack of investigative resource allocation and continued growth in illicit trade will continue. The need for education must extend to the 'front line', for there is a vital need for the reporting of suspected counterfeit or substandard products. It is the reports from the front line which will provide a proper assessment of the extent of the problem and build a picture that will identify offenders.

Enforcement

This is not simply a matter for police, customs and regulatory authorities. Proper enforcement involves market surveys and coordinated and prioritised investigations. In turn this will require industry-wide coordination of information, accepted reporting lines into public agencies and a clear agreement on roles and responsibilities within companies, the pharmaceutical industry (including parallel traders) and these public agencies. It also involves providing legislation that gives adequate powers to each of the public authorities charged with particular duties, and enabling adequate punishment for offenders.

Engineering

There is much that can be done through engineering to make it harder to sell counterfeit and substandard pharmaceuticals. Packaging design features, including minimum standards for repackaging, are important. The latest systems of tracking technology need to be embraced by the industry and encouraged by national governments. Engineering design of packaging, products and patient inserts is important, but without adequate forensic analysis of suspect items its power is lost. Few companies have adequate 'forensic' science capability, and the

UK Forensic Science Service would be ideally placed to lead on this issue, providing an interface between industry, law enforcement and prosecuting authorities (with their need to show scientific objectivity). Engineering also needs to encompass the review of production batch sizes to ensure that no batch is too large. The supply of batch numbers should provide a means of establishing where particular products have ended up or come from. Pharmaceutical companies, however, often use one batch number for thousands of products. When they are subsequently found in smaller consignments in the hands of reimporters it is often impossible to prove that it was this particular part of the batch which travelled around the world and was stored in inappropriate conditions. Smaller batch numbers would help solve this.

Design practices should also encompass 'soft engineering'. By this I mean those systems that are designed to protect companies, both manufacturers and parallel traders, from for instance entering into contracts with, or employing, individuals who have a criminal history demonstrating that they are unsuitable. Many companies continue to do business with others that have been shown to be inappropriate partners, and many companies still do not conduct pre-employment checks on their staff.

Finally, on the subject of engineering, when anti-counterfeiting design features are overcome by the counterfeiter, no company currently has a direct, easily identified and established 'feedback loop' to ensure that design modifications are routinely planned to keep ahead of the game. Evolution of product and packaging anti-counterfeiting design features is therefore, at best, intermittent, patchy, ad hoc and uncoordinated. Much more could be said in relation to how companies fail internally to collect and collate relevant information, and this naturally has an effect on their ability to respond intelligently. That problem is repeated across the pharmaceutical industry and serves only to conceal inadvertently the extent of the counterfeiting problem and make even more difficult any anti-counterfeiting investigation or initiative.

There have been many recommendations made recently as to how agencies can get to grips with these public health/crime problems. All need to be incorporated within a specific strategy. Below are some recommendations that flow from the author's experience and recent research. In addition, recommendations are reproduced from other sources as indicated.

For most of the last century, if someone advertised goods that too closely resembled branded goods, the aggrieved company could seek an injunction or take other legal remedy and manage the process using its marketing people and company lawyers. Such incidents were normally local or at worse national, but rarely international.

More recently, the Internet has provided instant global access to unlimited information about companies and brands as well as ever-evolving general and specialist sites for the sale of commercial and retail quantities of every type of branded goods. Think of any branded product and search the Internet. There it is in genuine form and perhaps also in counterfeit form.

Some years ago it was said that 'if in x years' time you are not doing business on the Web then you will not be doing business'. That time has now arrived. Look at the exponentially increasing growth in the use of the Internet and Internet sales.

Information, communication and business on the Internet, on a global scale, continues to spread.

Counterfeit products often come from parts of the world that make enforcement of rights (as we understand them) impossible for rights holders. In such countries, public enforcement agencies fail to see that protecting foreigners in the purchasing of medicines, even dangerous ones, is a significant problem for them. Their political leaders, through their inaction, seem to think likewise. In such circumstances there is invariably either no law to be enforced or no interest in enforcing such laws as do exist. This is sufficient to provide excellent opportunities and motivation for organised criminals to increase their involvement in pharmaceutical counterfeiting and diversion.

Medicines, as well as herbal remedies and all sorts of substandard products, are available at the press of an 'add to cart' button. Days later the item will be delivered, having travelled from Vanuatu, China or somewhere else that has no concept of consumer protection as we understand it. There are many developing countries where a substantial proportion of the population would love the luxury of being able to afford even substandard medicine. Such people are not yet, however, part of the consumer society. These countries simply do not protect their own citizens in the way we are protected at home. They do not invest in regulation or prosecution to prevent the export of such goods to us. They have greater priorities, which include earning foreign currency.

The only answer in such circumstances is provided at the political level, with our politicians speaking to theirs directly and via international groups. So it is that, for instance, the World Trade Organisation and agreements made under its auspices, such as TRIPS (the Treaty on Trade-Related Aspects of Intellectual Property Rights), and the UN (especially the WHO) have a vital role to play in bringing pressure to bear on countries that aspire to be part of a properly conducted international free-market community. Such countries need adequate legislation, adequate regulatory and enforcement regimes and adequate motivation to enforce the law once it is created.

The WHO factsheet states: 'Since the opening up of trade barriers between countries has led to an increase in counterfeiting, consistent and systematic efforts are needed at the international level. These should include the timely and appropriate exchange of information and the harmonization of measures to prevent the spread of these phenomena.'[1]

Action is therefore needed both at national and pan-European level.

Governments should:

➤ Formally consult with all interested parties to review the current methods for allowing the importation of pharmaceutical products, including Internet purchases (commercial or personal).

➤ Ensure that suitable primary and/or secondary legislation is available to regulators and police/customs to provide sufficient regulation and punishment for breaches.

➤ Take the lead to ensure that industry, both manufacturers and parallel traders, takes reasonable steps to identify counterfeit and substandard medicines and that resources are available to assist identification of counterfeits as a source of adverse drug reactions.

➤ Bring pressure to bear (both directly and indirectly) on

countries that either do not have adequate IP protection or choose not to enforce IP rights.

➤ Review the effectiveness of the law in relation to the obtaining of prescription medicines (commercial or consumer) on the Internet.

➤ Review the regulations that allow for the removal of brand-owner packaging and anti-counterfeiting features, consider a requirement for over-packaging only, and add a requirement for reasonable tamper-evident security features on both.

➤ More broadly on repackaging, the report *Design for Patient Safety* produced by the Design Council and the Department of Health (2004) identified the medical packaging and repackaging issue as one that plays a significant contributory role in causing suffering and death. It states: 'there is huge potential to reduce suffering and avoidable death, if we pay greater attention to safety and quality in design'. The report goes on to describe the need to develop adequate patient safety guidelines for packaging design to help reduce the medication errors that arise from, among other things, inconsistent or confusing packaging of medicines.

➤ Ensure that the public is made aware of the dangers and implications of buying pharmaceutical products from abroad on the Internet.

➤ Ensure that politicians are more aware of the potential for public harm and drive change in the interests of the public good.

➤ Ensure that as a society we:

  – Understand the nature and extent of the problems.

- Establish exactly where the threat comes from – geographically, internally and externally.
- Educate the public to help minimise the problems through greater awareness.
- Enlist the help of the media, trade organisations and others who have influence at the political level.

Meanwhile, in Europe and other Western countries, law enforcement is usually at best a matter for national agencies, local and under-resourced. Nowhere is it truly international. In the UK, the MHRA is trying to tackle, with inadequate resources and managerial expertise in dealing with major crime, what the large police forces and national crime squads fail to recognise as a significant or pertinent challenge.

Regulators and law enforcement agencies

To be in tune with evolving patterns of criminality, international law enforcement strategy needs to be in touch with what is happening 'on the streets' at operational level. Operational intelligence should inform the development of strategy, and strategy should determine operational direction. Therefore, in any truly concerted international law enforcement effort we should be able to trace two-way information flow from international to local level.

International law enforcement

Among the recommendations made by Interpol during 2004 were the following:

- Good practice and successful models for investigating IP crime nationally should be established.

- Interpol should work to reduce organised crime involvement in IP crime and reduce the risk that IP crime becomes a preferred source of terrorist financing.

- The need to allocate resources to the investigation of IP crime and to trace the proceeds of it should be more widely recognised.

- Interpol should help to coordinate international action against IP crime based on professional law enforcement and intelligence agency investigations into terrorist involvement in IP crime and other forms of criminality.

- The work of the Interpol Intellectual Property Crime Action Group (IPCAG) should be enhanced and developed by including a wide range of stakeholders from customs, police and private industry.

Under the auspices of Interpol the group should continue to address the following IP crime enforcement issues:

- Interpol's 181 member countries should each identify a national law enforcement IP crime central point of contact to facilitate the exchange of IP-crime-related information.

- Enhancing the exchange of information and intelligence on IP crime between law enforcement agencies.

- Enhancing and strengthening the operational contact network of private and public partners throughout Interpol's four regions – Africa, the Americas, Asia and Europe.

➤ Developing and disseminating the IP crime best practice guide; developing and delivering training in IP crime investigations to law enforcement agencies.

➤ Raising awareness of the issue of IP crime and its link to terrorist organisations and serious organised crime.

➤ Establishing 'a three-year private/public IP crime programme of activities. It will be coordinated by a dedicated IP Crime Unit at the General Secretariat and supported throughout Interpol's 181 Member States by a network of dedicated IP crime liaison officers located in the four Interpol Regions. The aim of the programme will be to develop and maintain a private/public IP crime partnership to:

  – Develop strategies and programmes to combat international criminal activity linked to IP infringement.
  – Raise awareness of IP crime and its links to terrorism and serious organised crime.
  – Facilitate and improve the exchange of information and intelligence on IP crime; coordinate international cross-border multi-agency investigations into IP crime.

The main commercial driving forces behind Interpol's involvement in counterfeiting have been the computer software companies, particularly Microsoft, the music industry and the tobacco industry. All have taken the problem of counterfeiting very seriously for several years and have invested accordingly. What is now needed, however, is a prioritisation process for the allocation of publicly funded law enforcement resources. Ultimately, both Interpol and domestic agencies will need to decide on which aspect of the counterfeiting problem they will spend their time. One would hope that they would regard a model that results in the avoidance of death and injury to thousands of citizens as being rather closer to the top of the list than music, tobacco or other non-essential branded goods.

Of course, Interpol is not a police force. It does not have agents out on the streets conducting investigations. Interpol is a valuable think tank, a repository for intelligence and a coordinator of arrangements, but ultimately the operational success of its schemes relies on national agencies.

The First World Customs Organisation (WCO) Global Congress on Combating Counterfeiting was held in May 2004 in Brussels. The outcome of this congress was at one with the Interpol position stated above. So much common ground was established that if any corroboration of the conclusions and recommendations of the head of Interpol were needed, then it was supplied by the congress. It recommended the universal adoption of the Interpol Intellectual Property Crime Model.

The congress also reported that:

1 The WCO is developing a Supply Chain Security Initiative and has identified counterfeit products as high-risk goods.

2 There is increasing awareness of the dangers of counterfeit pharmaceuticals and other drug products, not only on the part of the pharmaceutical industry but also that of the World Health Organisation and some national governments. They are initiating programmes to safeguard the drug supply chain and make consumers aware of the risks of counterfeit products.[2]

National law enforcement

Up to now most significant international investigations into counterfeit and other substandard pharmaceuticals reaching the UK and Europe have been conducted by investigators employed by the pharmaceutical companies. At national level (and, of course, beyond) there has been no public agency capable of or willing to gather intelligence or evidence on particular cases across international jurisdictions. Sometimes particular officers have shown willing and offered valuable help. It is almost always the case, however, that international police cooperation, where it has occurred in a counterfeiting investigation, has been the result of strenuous corporate investigative efforts, both in gathering intelligence and evidence and in presenting it to the right officials in the right way and at the right time.

There are two national agencies within the UK that are the natural 'owners' of international pharmaceutical counterfeiting enquiries concerning this country. They are the National Crime Squad and the National Criminal Intelligence Service. Neither has developed a strategy to serve the hopes, intentions, recommendations or aspirations of Interpol as outlined above. Importantly, however, NCIS is fully signed up to participate in the UK Patent Office initiative referred to above. In NCIS-speak, pharmaceutical counterfeiting is 'Level 3 Crime' – it involves serious and organised crime and international movement, and should therefore be a true priority, even if the first result of such prioritisation is simply to perform a 'baseline assessment' of the current risk.

For many brand-owners, access to NCIS or NCS is not something that they can easily gain. Many simply telephone their local police station. Horror stories abound. A tale of international counterfeiting of branded goods is usually met with a response of a few words from the local bobby, desk sergeant or civilian receptionist which clearly indicates that 'that's a civil matter' or 'that's one for Trading Standards', or simply 'we don't deal with that'.

Law enforcement and regulatory agencies need to establish the extent of this sort of crime and work together to share intelligence and take adequate action. Trading Standards offices vary greatly across the UK, and while they often employ excellent and dedicated people, they are never resourced sufficiently, nor do they have the remit to take on large-scale investigations. There is a growing awareness (the author gave a presentation to the UK Minister for Trade and Industry six years ago to this effect) that counterfeiting is linked to organised crime and terrorism. Yet our major law enforcement and intelligence agencies still regard themselves as too busy elsewhere to get involved.

The principal regulatory authority is the MHRA. Their role is absolutely vital. They need to:

1 Review again the yellow card scheme to ensure that healthcare professionals, the pharmaceutical industry and patients can report both adverse reactions and packaging and tampering concerns or errors in sufficient detail to enable meaningful analysis leading to identification of potential counterfeit products and enabling prioritisation of efforts. In 2004, a major review of the yellow card scheme was carried out and improvements were made, but the essential need to gather information on apparent adverse reactions to 'established' pharmaceutical products,

as opposed to new products, was overlooked. It also remains the case that no specific questions are being asked that would point towards identifying counterfeits or the importers of products that have caused harm.

2 Find the resources to be able to carry out more inspections on parallel importers.

3 Find the resources to become proactive in the analysis of data, launching intelligence-gathering operations and liaising with national police agencies. They also need to encourage the submission of market test data, relating to both packaging and products, to facilitate this aspect of necessary 'trend analytical work', using these sources as well as adverse reaction reports.

4 Consider providing extra staff on the basis that the user pays. This should be viewed as a reasonable tax on rights holders and importers.

5 Review the security and process of the supply chain, making recommendations for improvement in regulation and coordinating with the WCO initiative referred to above.

The judiciary
The judiciary need to understand the potential and actual consequences of these offences and punish them accordingly.

The Crown Prosecution Service (CPS)
The CPS, like others in the criminal justice system, seems to fail to see the significance of the problem of counterfeited pharmaceuticals. There needs to be a much greater awareness

of the potential for harm, and a much greater willingness to bring the most appropriate charges. Charges of fraud, criminal deception or forgery might allow for greater speed and certainty (on the basis that these are charges that are well known to the CPS), and in the short term may enable a suitably significant penalty, but they do nothing to highlight the value of appropriate legislation and conceal from view the true extent of this sort of crime.

On other occasions lesser regulatory charges are brought. Without the benefit of significant deterrent punishments, counterfeiting will continue to be, for the unscrupulous, a risk worth taking. Without adequate and appropriate charges against defendants, the judiciary are disempowered from punishing adequately.

Brand-owners

Brand-owners are often too conservative to attack the problem. There are very few major pharmaceutical companies that want to establish and publicise the nature and extent of the counterfeiting problem. Pfizer is currently the notable exception, though there may be others.

Most pharmaceutical companies seem stuck in a rut, believing that if they tell the world about counterfeiting problems experienced with one of their products then market share will be lost to a competitor. This seems to have become standard thinking. It might be more appropriate to:

➤ Assess to what extent the item is being counterfeited.

➤ Estimate the value of lost sales resulting.

➤ Obtain a legal opinion on any exposure to negligence that might result from lack of action.

➤ Consider the 'brand trust' and enhanced 'company image' that go with warning the public of imitations.

➤ Invest sufficient funds to reduce the problem.

➤ Work with other pharmaceutical companies and public authorities towards the public good.

At a two-day conference on this subject held in Spain earlier this year, Dr Lembit Rago, WHO's coordinator of quality assurance and safety of medicines, called for more transparency, saying the drugs industry had a great deal of data but was 'very reluctant to make [it] available'.[3]

➤ Pharmaceutical companies in Europe should be required to report to the appropriate national agency all information on counterfeit and suspected counterfeit drugs which comes to their attention, wherever in the world the incident has occurred.

➤ All European packs, irrespective of the language they are printed in to serve the needs of the intended market, should also be printed in common European languages. This regulatory requirement should prevail across Europe. This would, in practice, prevent the need for parallel traders to 'repack' the vast majority of products.

➤ Pharmaceutical companies do no routine 'market testing' for counterfeit or diverted products in the UK and very little elsewhere in Europe. Where market testing does take place, it is minimal, ad hoc and poorly coordinated. A standard model for the market testing of pharmaceuticals (an industry standard) would be invaluable as a method of early warning and would be of value not only to the consumer but to law enforcement and the industry.

➤ European packs should be RFID-tagged. Radio Frequency Identification tags would go a long way to enabling rights holders, traders, wholesalers, pharmacists and other interested parties to trace the true date of manufacture and place of origin of prescribed drugs. RFID tagging would involve the placing of a unique tag in the packaging of each product at the point of manufacture. Each tag would be capable of holding all the required electronic data and of being read by remote radio frequency link to establish the unique identity of the object to which the tag is attached. The principle is similar to a bar code operation. But the vital distinctions are:

- with RFID, more information can be stored and read;
- the reader is capable of reading numerous tags simultaneously;
- unlike with the bar code system, the RFID reader does not need to be near the item and does not need to 'see' the information it is reading (it is not read optically);
- bar codes only determine the type or identify a batch of products;
- RFID can identify every single separate product;
- RFID tags cannot be easily forged or copied.

From a patient safety perspective there are two critical points concerning the supply chain: first, the authenticity and age of the product as proven by evidence of when it left the genuine manufacturing site; second, verification of that information at the point at which the patient receives it. If this can be achieved then it will represent a major step forward.

The pilot scheme currently planned in the UK by PA Consulting will seek to authenticate products at the point of dispensing, permitting pharmacists to check immediately that the product has not been subject to recall, counterfeiting, diversion or other fraudulent activity and is within its shelf-life.

For pharmaceutical manufacturers, this initiative could provide a simple solution that will facilitate communications on matters of product recall in a matter of minutes and quickly identify suspect supply of products, allowing rapid action and investigation. Vitally, if the pharmaceutical industry were to coordinate its activities in this area, it would also enable much better coordination of intelligence on counterfeiting supply.

PA Consulting is offering to provide the infrastructure and support for the duration of the tagging pilot. It will involve a number of hospital and retail pharmacies and dispensing doctors. Yet the project needs the participation of the pharmaceutical manufacturers. All the pharmaceutical companies have to do is supply a range of pack types for inclusion.

According to a Parliamentary Office of Science Technology 'Postnote' dated July 2004 (no. 225): 'Large retail companies are driving for widespread adoption of RFID tagging as a way of achieving complete supply chain visibility. They see such technology as a way of preventing "out-of-stock" occurrences, and overstocking.' Let us hope that such companies will yet include among their number the pharmaceutical manufac-turers. The report continues: 'healthcare and commercial services industries are predicted to be the fastest-growing RFID sectors'.

RFID tagging could have a significant impact in minimising the opportunities for counterfeit, out-of-date and inadequately repackaged pharmaceuticals to reach consumers. A robust and industry-wide standard of RFID pharmaceutical tagging, accompanied by a secure database of information, managed centrally by reliable third parties, both within the spirit and according to the letter of the Data Protection Act, would clearly be in the public interest.

As Peter Lowe (assistant director of the Counterfeiting Intelligence Bureau, part of the International Chamber of Commerce) rightly pointed out earlier this year, companies are sensitive about sharing data on pharmaceutical counterfeiting because they think that raising awareness of the issue could unsettle patients and make them worry about whether the drugs they are taking are fake, and the lack of information does not help in trying to solve the problem. He said: 'There has to be a balance in there somewhere.' The implication is clear – that balance has not yet been achieved.[4]

Parallel traders

Such traders should:

1 Cooperate in putting an end to the practice of removing products from their original manufacturer's packaging and instead develop techniques of 'over-boxing'.

2 Take full and active part in routine batch recording and embrace new technologies such as RFID.

3 Work with the MHRA to ensure that their batch recall processes are reliable and robust.

4 Get accustomed to reporting to the MHRA any suspicious transactions or activity of which they become aware.

The US FDA report

The 2004 US FDA report *Combating Counterfeit Drugs* describes the inter-disciplinary meetings that were held in the USA to counter the fake pharmaceuticals threat to the US public. Evidence was taken from security experts, federal and state law enforcement officials, IT developers, manufacturers, wholesalers, retailers, consumer groups and the general public. Significant recommendations were made and explained. What follows here is a summary of the points that are most pertinent to the UK and Europe.

Technology

Implementation of new technologies to better protect our drug supply. Because the capabilities of counterfeiters continue to evolve rapidly, there is no single 'magic bullet' technology that provides any long-term assurance of drug security. However, a combination of rapidly improving 'track and trace' technologies and product authentication technologies should provide a much greater level of security for drug products in the years ahead.

[The adoption and common use of reliable track and

trace technology] would help secure the integrity of the drug supply chain by providing an accurate drug 'pedigree', which is a secure record documenting [that] the drug was manufactured and distributed under safe and secure conditions.

Radiofrequency Identification (RFID) tagging of products by manufacturers, wholesalers, and retailers appears to be the most promising approach to reliable product tracking and tracing. Significant feasibility studies and technology improvements are under way to confirm that RFID will provide cost-reducing benefits in areas such as inventory control, while also providing the ability to track and trace the movement of every package of drugs from production to dispensing. Most importantly, reliable RFID technology will make the copying of medications either extremely difficult or unprofitable.

Authentication technologies include measures such as colour shifting inks, holograms, fingerprints or chemical markers embedded in a drug or its label. The use of one or more of these measures on drugs, starting with those considered most likely to be counterfeited, is an important part of an effective anti-counterfeiting strategy. FDA plans to publish draft guidance on notification procedures for making changes to products, their packaging, or their labelling, for the purpose of encouraging timely adoption and adaptation of effective technologies for detecting counterfeit drugs. FDA also intends to continue to evaluate and provide information to stakeholders on forensic technologies (e.g., use of product fingerprinting, addition of markers) and other analytical methods that allow for rapid authentication of drug products.

Laws and regulation

Adoption of secure business practices by all participants in the drug supply chain – drug producers, distributors, and dispensers – to secure their business practices such as ensuring the legitimacy of business partners and refusing to do business with persons of unknown or dubious background, taking steps to ensure physical security, and identifying an individual or team in the organisation with primary responsibility for ensuring that effective security practices are implemented and supporting the development of industry best practices. To help ensure secure business practices, FDA intends to increase its inspection efforts of re-packagers whose operating procedures place them at increased risk for the introduction of counterfeit drugs.

Reporting

Development of a system that helps ensure effective reporting of counterfeit drugs to the agency and that strengthens [a] rapid response to such reports. If counterfeit drugs do enter the marketplace, procedures should be in place to recognize the hazard and alert the public quickly and effectively.

Collaboration with foreign stakeholders

> ... to develop strategies to deter and detect counterfeit
> drugs globally. Counterfeit drugs are a global challenge
> to all nations, and criminal counterfeiting operations
> are increasingly operating across national borders.

About five years ago, I was the main creator of a 'Memorandum of Understanding' between police forces in England and
Wales and other public and numerous private organisations and
companies. It attempted to provide for a joint effort against
counterfeit products in the UK. I did not imagine that things
would change quickly. But in view of the growing significance of the counterfeiting of branded products, it would not
be unreasonable to expect that more should be done by the
key players – law enforcement agencies and brand-owners –
to protect the consumer against what is a growing, sick and
exploitative business.

Appendix

Counterfeiting cases

The following are edited news reports of counterfeit drug cases.

FDA warns consumers about counterfeit drugs purchased in Mexico

30 July 2004

FDA Talk Paper

The FDA is warning the public about counterfeit versions of the drugs Zocor (simvastatin) and carisoprodol that were recently imported from Mexico by individual Americans. Tests indicate that the counterfeit Zocor did not contain any active ingredient and that the counterfeit carisoprodol differed in potency when compared to the authentic product. Carisoprodol is a drug used in the treatment of painful musculoskeletal conditions and Zocor is a cholesterol lowering drug. The counterfeit versions were reportedly purchased at Mexican border town pharmacies and sold. Patients who rely on these counterfeit versions of the drugs could develop serious health risks or have insufficient pain relief.

FDA has repeatedly expressed its concern about the purchase by Americans of drugs from foreign countries. As demonstrated by this incident, purchasers cannot assume that the products meet the quality, efficacy, and safety standards of FDA authorized products or that FDA is assuring the quality, safety, and efficacy of products purchased from outside the United States.

Medications purchased within the US system for prescription drugs have undergone rigorous testing and review to verify their identity, potency, purity and integrity during shipment so to ensure that they are safe and effective for their intended use.

FDA is investigating this matter and working with the Mexican authorities to ensure that further sale and importation of these products is halted.

Alarm over bogus drugs in Kenya

18 July 2004; posted to the Web 19 July 2004
Mburu Mwangi, Nairobi

The Government has moved to contain a public health scare by withdrawing drugs meant for distribution to public hospitals on claims that they are contaminated. The Director of Medical Services, Dr James Nyikal, said the painkillers were suspected to be laced with chalk and mouldy. 'We have ordered investigations into the matter after recalling the batch,' he said. If the tablets are found to be defective, the Ministry of Health will take the matter up with the supplier.

Investigations into the claims were being carried out by the drugs registration and quality control organisation, Pharmacy and Poisons Board. The alarm was raised by the Kenya Medical Supplies Agency (Kemsa) – which receives all drugs before they are distributed to hospitals, clinics and dispensaries [after the drugs had been distributed countrywide].

The suppliers won a tender to supply 25,000 boxes of the tablets, but it is claimed only 8,000 were genuine, while the rest were said to be contaminated. They are packaged to look like those of the genuine manufacturer before being supplied to Kemsa. The drugs were manufactured in November 2003 and are to expire in October 2007.

According to Kemsa, the first batch was taken to the Nyeri depot where it was to be distributed to health institutions in Central province. By the time the alarm was raised, the drugs had been distributed to Government health facilities throughout the country.

A system overwhelmed: the avalanche of imported, counterfeit, and unapproved drugs in the US – cases reported to the FDA

24 June 2003
William K. Hubbard (Associate Commissioner for Policy and Planning) and John M. Taylor, III (Associate Commissioner for Regulatory Affairs), Food and Drug Administration
Before the Subcommittee on Oversight and Investigations, Committee on Energy and Commerce, House of Representatives

Procrit

On May 21, 2003, the US Attorney's Office for the Southern District of Florida filed charges against Eddy Gorrin, William Chavez and Duviel Gonzalez for unlawful sale and wholesale distribution of counterfeit versions of Amgen, Inc.'s prescription drug Procrit, a medication indicated mainly to help cancer, anemia and HIV patients increase their red blood cell count.

Between January and February 2003, Gorrin intentionally engaged in the sale of counterfeit versions of Procrit. During that same time period, Chavez and Gonzalez also were engaged in unlawful wholesale distribution of counterfeit Procrit without a state licence. The vials being distributed by all three men labelled as 'Procrit' did not contain any active ingredient for Procrit, but instead, contained only bacteria-tainted water. In early June 2003 all three defendants plead guilty to criminal charges in the Southern District of Florida. The defendants face up to 10 years in prison and a $250,000 fine.

Lipitor

On May 23, 2003, FDA issued an alert on a counterfeit version of Pfizer, Inc.'s prescription drug, Lipitor. The alert warned health care providers and others that three lots of counterfeit Lipitor represent a potentially significant risk to consumers. One in five people have high cholesterol that may lead to cardiovascular disease, such as heart disease and stroke. Lipitor is the number one prescribed cholesterol-lowering medication, and is currently used by more than 18 million people.

On June 3, 2003, FDA announced that its continuing investigation of counterfeit Lipitor identified additional counterfeit quantities of the cholesterol-lowering product. The investigation is ongoing.

Serostim (somatropin (rDNA origin)) for injection

In late 2000 and early 2001, FDA became aware of consumer complaints about adverse effects and a recall was initiated at the distributor level for Serostim, a growth hormone often used to treat AIDS wasting. After further investigation by the manufacturer, Serono, Inc., and FDA, Serono issued press releases regarding the apparent counterfeiting of two lots of the product. In May 2002, Serono became aware that counterfeit Serostim displaying a fake lot number again had been distributed. Laboratory analysis by FDA showed that the product contained no active ingredient, and that the product did not originate from Serono.

Neupogen (filgrastim) for injection

In the spring of 2001, based on observations by a distributor about the appearance of Neupogen, a colony stimulating factor used mostly in cancer patients, the manufacturer, Amgen Inc., analyzed a suspect lot and determined that the vials contained only saline solution. The counterfeit product was labeled with fake lot numbers and/or wrong expiration dates.

Epogen (epoetin alfa) for injection

In May 2002, FDA, state regulators and the manufacturer, Amgen Inc., became aware that a potential counterfeit of Epogen was in commerce. The product, Epogen, is used to stimulate red blood cell production in cancer and AIDS patients. Amgen analysis indicated that certain vials of a

counterfeit product labeled as Epogen contained active ingredient approximately 20 times lower than expected. Further
investigation revealed that a major wholesale distributor was
holding approximately 1,600 cartons of counterfeit product.
Later that month, Amgen warned health care professionals
that two additional counterfeit lots of Epogen had been
discovered.

Combivir (lamivudine plus zidovudine) tablets

In the spring of 2002, GlaxoSmithKline (GSK) received four
complaints that bottles containing 60 tablets of Combivir
had been replaced with Ziagen tablets. In addition, the firm
determined that counterfeit Combivir labels had been placed
on authentic bottles of Ziagen tablets, a different GSK product
with a label containing a black box warning about the dangers
of possible fatal hypersensitive reactions to Ziagen. A black box
warning is the strongest warning to prescribing physicians,
health care professionals and consumers, that severe adverse
reactions have been experienced from use of the product. Both
Combivir and Ziagen can be used as part of a combination
regimen to treat HIV infection. The concern in this case was that
if an individual were to take the wrong tablet and is sensitive to
Ziagen, a potentially life-threatening hypersensitivity reaction
could occur. In May 2002 distributors were advised to initiate a
recall to their customers.

Zyprexa (olanzapine) tablets

In the winter and spring of 2002, bottles of Zyprexa, an Eli
Lilly and Company product, indicated for the treatment of
schizophrenia and acute bipolar mania, had been emptied and

refilled with white tablets. The tampering situations occurred in two strengths and in three different lots. In May 2002 Lilly issued a press release and Dear Health Care Professional letter concerning the tampering situation.

Offshore firms selling diluted, fake drugs as Canadian, FDA warns in battle over cheap imports

15 July 2004

Barrie McKenna, Washington

Americans are being duped by rogue Internet pharmacies in distant places such as British Columbia, China and Belize that masquerade as Canadian businesses and sell potentially dangerous fake and unregulated drugs, US regulators say. FDA commissioner William Hubbard told a US Senate committee yesterday that it's probing at least two bogus sites billing themselves as Canadian-based and selling drugs identified as Canadian generics. The drugs themselves were shipped from an address in Texas.

Mr Hubbard said the bogus sites are exploiting cracks in Canadian and US regulation. And while he acknowledged Canadian regulators are co-operating with the FDA in combating counterfeiters and illegal drugstores, Ottawa's primary concern isn't the health of Americans. 'The Canadian government is not going to ensure the health and safety of Americans,' he told the committee.

This year, Americans are expected to buy $1-billion (US) worth of drugs from Canada, where prescription drugs can be up to 80 per cent cheaper.

Mr Hubbard said FDA and customs inspectors are struggling to cope with a deluge of Internet sales already and that the FDA cannot guarantee the safety of any imported drugs, including those from 'Canadian suppliers, those who purport to be Canadian or other foreign sources that they believe to be reliable.'

FDA test results of prescription drugs from bogus Canadian website show all products are fake and substandard

13 July 2004

FDA News

A Food and Drug Administration (FDA) analysis of three commonly prescribed drugs purchased from a Web site advertised as Canadian showed that so-called 'Canadian Generics' bought from the Web site were fake, substandard and potentially dangerous. One was a controlled substance. In light of these findings, FDA reiterates its strong concerns about purchasing prescription drugs online from unknown sources, even where the website looks legitimate.

'Canadian Generics' had been sending 'spam' emails promoting its products. The products were so-called 'generic' versions of Viagra, Lipitor, and Ambien. None of the three products has a US-approved generic version, and so all three drugs were unapproved and are not the same quality as those approved by the FDA for sale in the United States. 'Consumers who believe they are getting equivalent products from reputable sources are being misled and putting their health at risk [since the drugs were the wrong strength, didn't dissolve properly or were contaminated],' said FDA Acting Commissioner Dr Lester M. Crawford.

Ambien, a controlled substance (schedule IV), is approved for the short-term treatment of insomnia. The product FDA obtained online contained [up to double the labelled] active ingredient. Taking 'superpotent' Ambien puts patients at risk for central nervous system depression, especially in elderly or debilitated patients.

The so-called 'generic' Lipitor FDA purchased was insufficiently pure and subpotent, providing on average only 57 percent of the active ingredient claimed on the label. Clinically, subpotent product could present a long-term risk for the various complications of high cholesterol, such as heart disease.

Internet stores ship fake drugs to US, Congress unit finds

17 June 2004

Bloomberg

Internet pharmacies outside the US and Canada shipped fake versions of Pfizer Inc.'s Viagra impotence drug, Roche Holdings AG's Accutane acne treatment and Purdue Pharma Inc.'s OxyContin painkiller to the US, a test by the investigative arm of Congress showed.

Orders from 68 pharmacies in the US, Canada and 10 other countries also showed that 45 sold prescription drugs without requiring a prescription from a patient, and four shipped medications with improper packaging, according to a report by Congress's General Accounting Office. An unspecified number improperly sent medicines that require monitoring by a doctor, the study found. 'We observed questionable characteristics and business practices of some of the Internet pharmacies from which we received drugs,' the GAO report said. 'Most, but not all, involved other foreign pharmacies' outside of Canada and the US.

In April, the Wisconsin Department of Health and Family Services told three Canadian Internet pharmacies that they violated terms of an agreement to ship only US-approved drugs, the US Food and Drug Administration said yesterday. The medicines had been approved in Canada.

Not approved for US

In its report, the congressional accounting office said it found that 16 of 18 drugs that investigators bought from Canadian pharmacies weren't approved for sale in the US. All of them were chemically comparable, the report said. Investigators also obtained drugs from Argentina, Costa Rica, Fiji, India, Mexico, Pakistan, Philippines, Spain, Thailand and Turkey, according to the report. [Reported cases included Connecticut-based Purdue Parma's Oxycontin pain drug, Basel, Switzerland-based Novartis AG's Clozaril schizophrenia drug, Switzerland-based Roche's Accutane, which pregnant women shouldn't take because of the risk of stillbirth or deformities in their children.]

FDA takes action against foreign websites selling counterfeit contraceptive patches

Continuing investigation identifies three more suspect websites

12 February 2004

FDA News

FDA has taken action against three foreign internet sites associated with a site previously found to be selling counterfeit contraceptive patches that contain no active ingredients. These counterfeit patches provide no protection against pregnancy.

The three newly discovered internet sites involved are www.usarxstore.com, www.europeanrxpharmacy.com, and www.generic.com. These sites also sold other drugs that purported to be the same as FDA-approved drugs, but are in fact from unknown sources and of unknown safety and efficacy. To protect the public health FDA has obtained the cooperation of the US-based internet service provider in shutting down service to these sites. The counterfeit contraceptive patches were promoted as Ortho Evra transdermal patches, which are FDA approved, and made by Ortho-McNeil Pharmaceutical, Inc.

FDA urges consumers to treat any drugs purchased from these websites as suspect, and not to be considered safe or effective.

Instead customers receive packages of patches without the active ingredient necessary to make the patches effective. Moreover, the counterfeits were sent in simple plastic zip-lock bags without identifying materials, lot numbers, expiration dating or any other labeling information needed to safely and effectively use this prescription product.

The source of the products offered for sale and the safety and efficacy of those products are unknown. Distribution of these suspect products appears limited to the internet, and we cannot be certain that sales are limited to only the four sites identified to date.

FDA and Johnson & Johnson warn public about counterfeit contraceptive patches sold through foreign internet site

4 February 2004

FDA News

FDA and Johnson & Johnson of Raritan, NJ are warning the public about an overseas internet site selling counterfeit contraceptive patches that contain no active ingredients. These counterfeit patches provide no protection against pregnancy.

This internet site's domain name, www.rxpharmacy.ws, apparently is operated by American Style Products of New Delhi, India. The site also sells other products that purport to be versions of FDA-approved drugs. FDA is investigating these other products as well, and urges consumers to treat any drugs purchased from this firm as being suspect. None of these products should be considered safe or effective.

The FDA-approved Ortho Evra contraceptive patch is an adhesive patch that contains a combination of an estrogen and a progestin for contraception. The patch is applied to the skin of a woman's abdomen, upper outer arm, upper torso or buttock for seven days. A new patch is applied each week for three weeks (21 total days), followed by one patch-free week.

The FDA-approved patch product is 1¾ inches square, beige in color, made of a thin film, and comes packaged in a sealed, opaque, white pouch with the product label attached to one side of the pouch. The lot number and expiration date for the product are printed on the attached label and on the backside of the pouch without the attached label.

The counterfeit product is 1½ inches square, brown in color, made of woven material, and has 5 holes that appear as red dots on the middle of the top side of the patch. This product also has a ¾ inch orange square resembling gauze under the plastic liner on the backside of the patch. The product does not come packaged in a sealed pouch and does not contain lot number or expiration date information.

FDA issues alert on counterfeit polypropylene mesh used in hernia repair

19 December 2003
FDA Talk Paper and FDA Alert
The FDA today alerted healthcare professionals to a counterfeit polypropylene mesh product labeled as PROLENE polypropylene mesh. The product is a non-absorbable mesh used in hernia repair and other surgery. The authentic PROLENE mesh is manufactured by Ethicon, Inc. Ethicon issued an alert to healthcare professionals about the counterfeit product on October 28.

The company noted several characteristics of the counterfeit product that may help to distinguish it from genuine PROLENE: a packaging seal that does not tear open smoothly; an additional small seal on top corner edges of the package; a fabric end that is jagged or not cleanly cut on the 3-inch side; and an ETHICON logo in a thicker than usual typeface.

Preliminary testing of the counterfeit PROLENE by FDA

indicates that some samples are not sterile and that the counterfeit product has a molecular structure similar to other polypropylene mesh products currently on the market. Although FDA has not had reports of excess infections with the counterfeit product, the agency continues to be concerned about sterility.

FDA alerts consumers and health professionals to recall of counterfeit Lipitor

23 May 2003

FDA Talk Paper

The FDA today announced that Albers Medical Distributors, Inc., has voluntarily recalled three lots of 90-count bottles of the cholesterol-lowering drug Lipitor and is warning healthcare providers and others that these three lots of counterfeit Lipitor represent a potentially significant risk to consumers. The product was repackaged by Med-Pro, Inc., of Lexington, Neb., and the labels say 'Repackaged by: MED-PRO, Inc. Lexington, Neb.' in the lower left-hand corner.

As part of the FDA's ongoing efforts to investigate and address unscrupulous counterfeiting activities, FDA's Office of Criminal Investigations is investigating the existence of counterfeit Lipitor. Lipitor is a member of a class of cholesterol-lowering drugs that are commonly referred to as 'statins'.

FDA's investigation into this matter is continuing.

Serono issues notification of counterfeit Serostim®

16 May 2002

FDA News Release, Rockland, MA

Serono, Inc. has recently become aware of a counterfeit lot of Serono's Serostim® [somatropin (rDNA origin) for injection]. The counterfeit material has been packaged to appear as drug product lot number S810-1A1. This is not a legitimate Serostim® lot number. Serono has notified the appropriate regulatory and law enforcement authorities of this matter.

Preliminary information appears to indicate that the counterfeit material may have been distributed via the Internet. However, Serono is also alerting pharmacists to the counterfeit material and recommending that they examine Serostim® prior to dispensing to ensure that the package does not bear lot number S810-1A1.

The counterfeit material was neither manufactured nor distributed by Serono. Therefore, it cannot be assumed that the counterfeit material is either safe or effective.

Serostim® is approved in the US for the treatment of AIDS wasting.

HSA detects counterfeit Cialis and cautions against buying from illegal sources

16 January 2004

Health Sciences Authority, Singapore

The Health Sciences Authority (HSA) has detected the presence of counterfeit Cialis tablets being sold by illegal peddlers in the black market. This was among the findings arising from recent joint operations conducted by HSA's Centre for Drug Administration and Singapore Customs' Special Investigation Branch, in which a total of four Chinese nationals were caught and various types of counterfeit and unregistered medicines were seized. Two of the offenders have already been charged and convicted in Court.

Cialis, which contains tadalafil, is a medicinal product indicated for the treatment of male erectile dysfunction. This product was registered with HSA in January 2003, and genuine Cialis is distributed locally by Eli Lilly (S) Pte Ltd [and its agents].

The counterfeit Cialis tablets seized by HSA are labelled to contain 20mg of tadalafil and have packaging which mimics that of the genuine product. However, analysis of the counterfeit tablets by HSA's Centre for Analytical Science found it to contain varying amounts of tadalafil mixed with sildenafil (another erectile dysfunction drug). The local distributor has confirmed that the packaging of the seized tablets differed from that of the genuine article and that the seized stocks are counterfeits.

Pfizer, FDA warn about fake Viagra in California

Thu 1 July, 2004 00:10
Lisa Richwine, Washington (Reuters)
US regulators warned on Wednesday that fake versions of Pfizer Inc.'s impotence pill Viagra had been found in two retail pharmacies in Glendale and Fresno, California. The FDA said it and

Pfizer 'are analyzing the counterfeit product to determine its true composition and whether it poses any health risks'.

'Only genuine Viagra is approved by the FDA and can be considered to be safe and effective,' Pfizer said in a letter to pharmacists that was posted on the company's Web site. Pfizer spokesman Byrant Haskins said 'there's nothing to suggest it's a widespread counterfeiting issue'.

The fake pills were discovered after a patient who bought Viagra at the Glendale pharmacy noticed unusual printing on the packaging and other variations, Haskins said. Tests confirmed those tablets were counterfeit. The fake tablets look similar to the real thing but have several deviations, the FDA said. For example, the counterfeit tablets have more pronounced edges and are a lighter blue than real ones.

Viagra, which had worldwide sales of nearly $1.9 billion last year, is a frequent target for counterfeiters. Pfizer said it was introducing new packaging designed to make the Viagra label harder for criminals to copy.

China gets tough on counterfeit medicine makers

2000

United Press International – www.applesforhealth.com

When Chi Suzhen, a 44-year-old cosmetics saleswoman, bought over-the-counter cold medicine for her 12-year-old daughter in September, she thought nothing of the safety of the drugs, which are commonly used by Chinese to treat mild illnesses.

Less than three days later, her daughter died from what doctors told her was a deadly dose of counterfeit medicine. Although the family made numerous attempts to find out how the poorly manufactured drugs had made it onto the store shelves, government officials were unable to provide answers.

'I thought these drugs were safe,' she said. 'No one told me, not even the doctors, to be concerned about fake medicines in the marketplace. There is no way to describe how sorrowful I feel having lost my only daughter.' The Chi family, who plan to sue the pharmacy that sold them the bogus medicine, is not alone in their grief. According to the Shanghai Drug Administration, drug poisonings killed an estimated 200,000 Chinese and hospitalised 2.5 million in 1999.

Officials blame counterfeit over-the-counter and prescription drugs – many of which they say contain raw, unprocessed ingredients – for the majority of the deaths. China has been getting tough on the manufacturers of counterfeit medicines in the country's $40 billion pharmaceutical market. In the past year, the central government has closed down at least 113 pharmaceutical factories and nearly 15,000 illegal drug distributors.

In Shanghai, home to a large majority of the country's drug manufacturing plants, city officials have come under increasing pressure to crack down on counterfeiters. In a highly symbolic move last week, officials destroyed 70,000 cases of counterfeit drugs, valued at RMB 2 million (US $2,240,000), and announced the creation of a special task force.

'Those bogus medicines, produced and sold by illegal factories and marketing offices, not only pose harm to public health, but also affect the dynamic development of the city's pharmaceutical industry,' Zhou Yupeng, Shanghai's vice mayor, said as a steam roller plowed over a pile of bogus medicine.

This year alone, the city's drug administration has prosecuted 28 cases that violated the medicine regulation. One prosecution involved 120 cases of pirated Tibet Rhodiola – an herbal medicine containing a powerful bioflavanoid – made by Huaxi Pharmaceutical (Group) Co. Ltd. Another concerned 2,185 cases of pirated Amoxycillin of the United Laboratories Ltd.

'The ingredients in those fake medicines aren't the same as those in legitimate drugs. The fakes are very dangerous and pose a threat to public health,' said Paul Li, managing director of Merck Sharp & Dohme (China) Ltd. 'We hope government will crack down on those bogus drugs as well as the smuggling, but so far their efforts have not been successful.'

Notes

Chapter 1: Introduction

1. Progress report and recommendations of the Eleventh
   International Conference of Drug Regulatory Authorities,
   16–19 February 2004, p. 20, www.who.int/medicines/library/
   qsm/icdra2004/ICDRA11reportApril12004.pdf.

2. *Counterfeit and Substandard Medicines*, WHO factsheet no. 275,
   February 2003, www.who.int/mediacentre/factsheets/fs275/
   en/print.html.

3. Ibid.

Chapter 2: Counterfeit drugs and the Internet

1. *A System Overwhelmed: the Avalanche of Imported, Counterfeit,
   and Unapproved Drugs in the US*, William K. Hubbard
   (Associate Commissioner for Policy and Planning) and
   John M. Taylor, III (Associate Commissioner for Regulatory
   Affairs), FDA, before the Subcommittee on Oversight and
   Investigations, Committee on Energy and Commerce, House
   of Representatives, 24 June 2003, www.fda.gov/ola/2003/
   importedrx0624.html.

Chapter 3: The growth in parallel trade

1. Social Market Foundation seminar held in January 2004 involving Dr Peter West, Dr Panos Kanavos and Jacob Arfwedson, all of whom have published papers on parallel trade. The proceedings of the seminar are available online. Niall Maclean (ed.), *Parallel Trade in Medicines: The Results of a Social Market Foundation Discussion Seminar*, Social Market Foundation, 2004, p. 9, www.smf.co.uk/site/smf/publications/paralleltrade/pdfFile.

2. J. Arfwedson, *Parallel Trade in Pharmaceuticals*, Centre for New Europe, 2003.

3. Data supplied by MHRA to author, August 2004.

4. S. Pollard, 'There Is No Such Thing as a Free Drug', *Wall Street Journal Europe*, 2 July 2004.

Chapter 4: The current regulatory and enforcement regime

1. *A Guide to the Implementation of EC Directive 92/25: Wholesale Distribution of Medicinal Products for Human Use in the European Community*, MCA, May 1993 (issued 2004), p. 4.

2. Ibid., para. 3.3, p. 22.

3. Ibid., para. 3.3 at v1.

4. *Notes for applicants and holders of a wholesale dealer's licence*, MCA, revised May 1999, para. 3.5.

5. N. Maclean, *Parallel Trades in Medicines*, Social Market Foundation, 2004, p. 4.

6. M. Pirmohamed et al., 'Adverse drug reactions as cause of admission to hospital: prospective analysis of 18,820 patients', *British Medical Journal*, 329, July 2004, p. 15.

7. Ibid., p. 19.

8. Ibid., p. 18.

9. www.npsa.nhs.uk.

10. National Patient Safety Agency, *Corporate Plan 2003–2004*, NPSA, 24 June 2003, p. 4.

11. Written response provided to author by Nick Rigg, Communications Directorate, NPSA, 21 July 2004.

Chapter 5: Opportunities in an under-policed environment

1. *A Spoonful of Sugar: Medicines Management in NHS Hospitals*, Audit Commission, 2001, p. 19, www.audit-commission.gov.uk/Products/NATIONAL-REPORT/E83C8921-6CEA-4b2c-83E7-F80954A80F85/nrspoonfulsugar.pdf.

2. *The links between intellectual property crime and terrorist financing*, text of the public testimony of Ronald K. Noble, Secretary-General of Interpol, before the United States House Committee on International Relations, 16 July 2003, www.interpol.int/public/ICPO/speeches/SG20030716.asp.

Chapter 6: Linking 'diversion', parallel trade and counterfeiting

1. *Counterfeit and Substandard Medicines*, WHO factsheet no. 275, February 2003, www.who.int/mediacentre/factsheets/fs275/en/print.html.

2. Ibid.

Chapter 7: The growth in illicit trade and counterfeiting

1. FDA, *Combating Counterfeit Drugs: a Report of the Food and Drug Administration*, February 2004, www.fda.gov/oc/initiatives/counterfeit/report0204.html.

2. The International Conference of Drug Regulatory Authorities meeting as reported in L. Gibson, 'Drug regulators study global treaty to tackle counterfeit drugs', *British Medical Journal*, 328, 28 February 2004.

3. *Counterfeit and Substandard Medicines*, WHO factsheet no. 275, February 2003, www.who.int/mediacentre/factsheets/fs275/en/print.html.

4. S. Carrell, 'A two-part investigation – Eastern Europe and Counterfeit Pharmaceuticals', *Independent on Sunday*, 18 January 2004.

5. Vladimir Shipkov, Russian Ministry of Health – Pharmaceuticals Inspectorate, who added that 321 pharmacies were closed in Russia in 2003 for manufacturing and dealing in fake medicines. Quoted in *The Russia Journal*, 25 October 2003.

6. Carrell, op. cit.

7. WHO, op. cit.

8. Central Statistical Office of Poland, www.stat.gov.pl/english/index.htm.

9. Ibid.

10. Indian high commission, Poland, as quoted on www.BisnetWorld.net, July 2004.

11. WHO, op. cit.

12. WHO, op. cit.

13. www.a-cg.org.

14. www.aacp.org.uk/cost/casestudies.html.

Chapter 9: Organised crime and terrorism

1. NCIS, *United Kingdom Threat Assessment of Serious and Organised Crime 2003*, www.ncis.co.uk/ukta/2003/ukta2003.pdf.

2. *Counterfeit and Substandard Medicines*, WHO factsheet no. 275, February 2003, www.who.int/mediacentre/factsheets/fs275/en/print.html.

3. European Federation of Pharmaceutical Industry Associations meeting, 2002.

4. Ibid. See *Federal Register*, 67(153), 8 August 2002.

5. ACAP, *Proving the Connection: Links between intellectual property theft and organised crime*, Alliance Against Counterfeiting and

Piracy, 2003, p. 1, www.aacp.org.uk/Proving-the-Connection. pdf.

6. Ibid.

7. Progress report and recommendations of the Eleventh International Conference of Drug Regulatory Authorities, 16–19 February 2004, www.who.int/medicines/library/qsm/ icdra2004/ICDRA11reportApril12004.pdf.

8. Report of the pre-Eleventh ICDRA satellite workshop on counterfeit drugs, 2004, p. 11, www.who.int/medicines/ organisation/qsm/activities/qualityassurance/cft/Pre-ICDRA_Counterfeit_report.pdf; L. Gibson, 'Drug regulators study global treaty to tackle counterfeit drugs', *British Medical Journal*, 328, 28 February 2004.

9. Report of the pre-Eleventh ICDRA satellite workshop, op. cit.; Gibson, op. cit.

10. Gibson, op. cit.

Chapter 10: Conclusions and recommendations

1. *Counterfeit and Substandard Medicines*, WHO factsheet no. 275, February 2003, www.who.int/mediacentre/factsheets/fs275/ en/print.html.

2. *Outcomes Statement of the First Global Congress on Combating Counterfeiting*, Brussels, May 2004, www.akjassociates.com/ wco2004/website.asp?page=declaration.

3. L. Gibson, 'Drug regulators study global treaty to tackle counterfeit drugs', *British Medical Journal*, 328, 28 February 2004.

4. Ibid.

Bibliography

Publications

Arfwedson, J., *Parallel Trade in Pharmaceuticals*, Centre for New Europe, 2003

Carrell, S., 'A two-part investigation – Eastern Europe and Counterfeit Pharmaceuticals', *Independent on Sunday*, 18 January 2004

Gibson, L., 'Drug regulators study global treaty to tackle counterfeit drugs', *British Medical Journal*, 328, 28 February 2004

Kanavos, P. et al., *The Economic Impact of Pharmaceutical Parallel Trade in European Union Member States: a Stakeholder Analysis*, LSE Health and Social Care, London School of Economics and Political Science, 2004, www.lse.ac.uk/collections/LSEHealthAndSocialCare/pdf/Workingpapers/executivesummary.pdf

Lister, S., 'At least 10,000 people die from reactions to everyday drugs', *The Times*, 2 July 2004

Maclean, N. (ed.), *Parallel Trade in Medicines: the Results of a Social Market Foundation Discussion Seminar*, Social Market Foundation, 2004, www.smf.co.uk/site/smf/publications/paralleltrade/pdfFile

Naik, G., 'Nigerian Regulator Dodges Violence to Fight Fake

Drugs: Dorothy Akunyili Speaks out against Bogus Medicines and Makers Lash Back', *Wall Street Journal*, 28 May 2004

Pirmohamed, M. et al., 'Adverse drug reactions as cause of admission to hospital: prospective analysis of 18,820 patients', *British Medical Journal*, 329: 15–19 July 2004

Pollard, S., 'There Is No Such Thing as a Free Drug', *Wall Street Journal Europe*, 2 July 2004

West, P., *Benefits to Payers and Patients from Parallel Trade*, York Health Economics Consortium, 2003

Reports

Alliance Against Counterfeiting and Piracy, *Proving the Connection: Links between intellectual property theft and organised crime*, 2003, www.aacp.org.uk/Proving-the-Connection.pdf

Anti-Counterfeiting Group, *Why You Should Care about Counterfeiting*, 2004

Audit Commission, *A Spoonful of Sugar: Medicines Management in NHS Hospitals*, 2001, www.audit-commission.gov.uk/Products/NATIONAL-REPORT/E83C8921-6CEA-4b2c-83E7-F80954A80F85/nrspoonfulsugar.pdf

Department of Health (UK), *An Organisation with a Memory: Report of an Expert Group on Learning from Adverse Effects in the NHS*, 2000

Department of Health (UK), *Building a Safer NHS for Patients – Improving Medication Safety*, 2004

Food and Drug Administration (US), *Combating Counterfeit Drugs: a Report of the Food and Drug Administration*, February 2004, www.fda.gov/oc/initiatives/counterfeit/report02_04.html

International Conference of Drugs Regulatory Authorities, *Progress Report and Recommendations of the Eleventh International*

Conference of Drug Regulatory Authorities, 16–19 February 2004, www.who.int/medicines/library/qsm/icdra2004/ICDRA11_reportApril2004.pdf

Interpol, *The links between intellectual property crime and terrorist financing*, text of the public testimony of Ronald K. Noble, Secretary-General of Interpol, before the United States House Committee on International Relations, 16 July 2003, www.interpol.int/public/ICPO/speeches/SG20030716.asp

Interpol Intellectual Property Crime Action Group, introductory leaflet, www.interpol.int/Public/FinancialCrime/IntellectualProperty/Publications/IIPCAG.pdf

Medicines and Healthcare Products Regulatory Authority (formerly Medicines Control Agency), *Notes for applicants and holders of a wholesale dealer's licence*, revised May 1999

Medicines and Healthcare Products Regulatory Authority (formerly Medicines Control Agency), *A Guide to the Implementation of EC Directive 92/25: Wholesale Distribution of Medicinal Products for Human Use in the European Community*, May 1993, issued 2004

National Criminal Intelligence Service (UK), *United Kingdom Threat Assessment of Serious and Organised Crime 2003*, www.ncis.co.uk/ukta/2003/ukta2003.pdf

National Patient Safety Agency, *Business Plan 2003–2004*, 8 May 2003

National Patient Safety Agency, *Corporate Plan 2003–2006*, 24 June 2003

World Customs Organisation, *Outcomes Statement of the First Global Congress on Combating Counterfeiting*, Brussels, May 2004, www.akjassociates.com/wco2004/website.asp?page=declaration

World Health Organisation, *Counterfeit and Substandard Medicines*, WHO Factsheet no. 275, February 2003, www.who.int/mediacentre/factsheets/fs275/en/print.html

World Health Organisation, *Report of the pre-Eleventh ICDRA*

satellite workshop on counterfeit drugs, www.who.int/medicines/
organisation/qsm/activities/qualityassurance/cft/Pre-ICDRA_
Counterfeit_report.pdf

Joining the Stockholm Network

Would you or your organisation like to join the Stockholm Network? We have varying levels of membership, depending on your needs and interests. For further information, please contact our Director of Development, Nicole Gray Conchar (nicole@stockholm-network.org).

Subscribe to the mailing list

Fancy getting a taste of what we do and what think tanks are doing right across Europe? The Stockholm Network's weekly e-newsletter rounds up the latest activities of Europe's leading think tanks and thinkers and provides a valuable summary of current policy trends across the EU. To sign up, contact Sacha James Kumaria (sacha@stockholm-network.org), or visit our website: www.stockholm-network.org.